The Ultimate
BABY
BOOK

The Ultimate BABY BOOK

by Joan Vos

A PLANNER FOR PREGNANCY AND BIRTH

EXETER BOOKS
NEW YORK

A QUARTO BOOK

Copyright © 1985 by Quarto Marketing Ltd.

First published in the USA 1985 by Exeter Books.
Distributed by Bookthrift
Exeter is a trademark of Simon & Schuster, Inc.
Bookthrift is a registered trademark of Simon & Schuster, Inc.
New York, New York

ISBN 0-671-07779-1

THE ULTIMATE BABY BOOK
was prepared and produced by
Quarto Marketing Ltd.
15 West 26th Street, New York, N.Y. 10010

Designer: Rod Gonzalez

Typeset by BPE Graphics, Inc.
Printed and bound in Hong Kong by Leefung-Asco Printers Ltd.

The Ultimate Baby Book: A Planner for Pregnancy and Birth is for informational purposes only and is not intended as an authoritative medical resource. Before entering any dietary, exercise, or medical program, or if any complications develop for you or your baby during or after your pregnancy, your physician should be consulted.

To Cornelia, my mother

SPECIAL THANKS TO

Angus for love, encouragement, and advice
Sylvan for advice and for having been a wonderful baby
Marta Hallett, my editor, for her bright sense of humor
Naomi Black for her faith and very good counsel

AND SPECIAL THANKS FOR THEIR CONTRIBUTIONS TO

Dr. Paula Ertel Feinstein, Developmental Psychologist
Christina Le Barre, Nurse Practitioner
Dr. Ramon Murphy, Pediatrician
Clio Perez, Holistic Health Counselor
Dr. Kathryn Schrotenboer, Gynecologist, Obstetrician, and Author

---

Beth Keillor and Sara Schaeffer of Simplicity Patterns
Diane Cardinale of Toy Manufacturers of America, Inc.
Carole Seskin of the Avalon Registry
Judy Torgus of La Leche League
Robert Goldberg, Assistant Director of Public Health Education March of Dimes Foundation
Mary Snyder of Snugli, Inc.
James Arey, System Director of Public Relations for Pan American Airlines
Dr. Weissman and Dr. Howland of the Poison Control Center, New York City Department of Health

Contents

INTRODUCTION

PLANNING A MIRACLE

Having a baby has been called an everyday miracle, and though this might sound like a contradiction in terms, there is no better way to describe it. Even though it happens to someone every day, when it happens to you it will be awe-inspiring and often bewildering. Even though 10,000 babies are born in the United States every day, when you are expecting your baby it will be a uniquely personal experience. A single cell becoming a complete human being is truly miraculous, and adjusting to the accompanying changes is a matter of careful and practical planning.

A full-term pregnancy lasts 280 days from the first day of your last period or 266 days from the approximate date of your last ovulation. To calculate your due date, add a year to the first day of your last period, then subtract three months, and then add a week. Delivery dates can vary but they can rarely be postponed just because you are not ready. From the moment of conception you have to plan for and prepare to give your baby the very best. There's so much to learn and arrange.

Planning means knowing what to expect of your body, of your baby, of your medical help, and of the people around you. Circumstances may vary, but a general working knowledge of what might happen can help you to feel confident and to make the right decisions. Without planning, some of the hormonal influences and practical aspects of pregnancy and early motherhood can overwhelm your attempts to organize your time and your thoughts. Use the checklists provided in this book to schedule activities and preparations, and check tasks off as you complete them. Use the Useful Addresses and Reading appendices to supplement your knowledge—they are listed by subject according to the order of the book.

It's very important to know what your options are. Without such information, you cannot make the best choices. Read everything of interest. Collect advice from experienced mothers and from medical experts. Ask questions and take notes, not only of what you read and hear but of your own feelings, dreams, and wishes. Use the pages provided throughout this book for your notes and observations. They make interesting reading in the years to come, and mothers-to-be should learn to value their intuitions and perceptions.

Every year, prenatal and pediatric care improves. Naturally you want the very best for your baby. Start planning and learning now—even if you're not pregnant yet. If you are already pregnant—CONGRATULATIONS! A child is a miracle that you can enjoy every day for many years to come.

CHAPTER ONE
THE FIRST MONTH

PHYSICAL CHANGES

It's not always easy to know if you are pregnant, although some women say, in retrospect, that they knew it all along. Pregnancy usually can't be confirmed until after the first four weeks, but a missed period increases the likelihood. Your breasts might feel full and tender during the first month. You might also feel nauseous or in need of a little extra rest. Any of these symptoms is a good reason for consulting a doctor.

As soon as you suspect you might be pregnant, take extra care. Avoid X-rays and medication unless they are prescribed by a doctor who knows that you might be pregnant.

PSYCHOLOGICAL CHANGES

Your emotions may fluctuate wildly at the time of your first missed period. If it feels like an embarrassing throwback to the woes and wonders of puberty, it's not surprising. There's a similar hormonal upheaval underway.

Try to laugh about it when you find yourself crying over a toothpaste commercial or wondering what you've gotten yourself into. This, too, will pass. You'll be able to keep your emotions in perspective once your body adjusts to its new state. Funny movies, funny books, and reassuring hugs can work wonders.

⚜ CHOOSING A DOCTOR

The best time to choose an obstetrician is before you become pregnant. The first twelve weeks—the first trimester—of your pregnancy is a most important and delicate time in your baby's development. If you suspect that you are pregnant, confirm it as soon as possible and begin prenatal care.

A good way to find a doctor is through recommendations. A friend who has just had a baby may suggest a doctor whose ideas on care and delivery are compatible with yours. Your family doctor/general practitioner or any other doctor you trust can recommend someone whose medical reputation is good. Obstetricians are certified by the *American College of Obstetricians and Gynecologists* (ACOG), which will supply referrals upon request.

Other good sources are the *Directory of Medical Specialists* and your state's directory of specialists. These sources include such information as your doctor's training, place of internship, hospital affiliations, and teaching duties (teaching can be an indication that your doctor is up to date on the latest medical developments).

If you have heard good things about a hospital in your area, you can call their Obstetrics/Gynecology (OB/GYN) unit and ask for a referral to a doctor who admits patients there or an obstetrical clinic based there. You can look up your prospective hospital in the *American Hospital Association Guide to Health Care Field,* which lists the facilities of all hospitals certified by the Joint Commission of Accreditation of Hospitals. If you want to know specifics about your hospital—Do they allow rooming-in? Is there a birthing room?—the OB/GYN department is usually happy to supply the information.

You may want to be delivered by your family doctor, you may want to have your baby in a birthing center, or you may want to give birth at home with a midwife. If you already know that you would prefer a "natural" or "prepared" childbirth, contact the *American Society for Psychoprophylaxis in Obstetrics* for the name of an affiliated health care professional. If you would like to be delivered at home by a midwife, contact the *American College of Nurse-Midwifery* for information. A birthing center is another option. *The National Association of Childbearing Centers* will tell you what is available in your area and give you guidelines for measuring the standards of birthing centers. (See the Useful Addresses appendix).

Some physical conditions make pregnancy a somewhat risky business. A woman who suffers from any of the following conditions may fall into the high risk category, and should contact an appropriate medical specialist as early in her pregnancy as possible. Medical supervision may be required if you fall into one of the high risk categories.

HIGH RISKS
- diabetes
- heart disease
- epilepsy
- high blood pressure
- previous obstetrical complications

INTERVIEWING THE DOCTOR

When you find one or more suitable doctors or health care professionals, the next step is to arrange interviews. If you don't feel comfortable with your doctor, no matter how well qualified and competent, you won't have a good working relationship. You must feel that you can call your doctor any time you have a question about your pregnancy. Your anxieties are a normal part of caring for your unborn child and must be treated accordingly. Discuss any questions and concerns you have with the doctor you are interviewing and take notes, mental or written, on your impressions of the answers you get. A doctor who intimidates you is the wrong doctor.

You might get lucky and like the first doctor you see. If for any reason you don't, shop around until you do find someone you feel comfortable with. You wouldn't hire a housekeeper or a secretary based on one interview unless you had an overwhelmingly favorable first impression. So why settle for a doctor you're not satisfied with, particularly since you two will share such an important event?

You might get halfway through your pregnancy and decide a change is in order. Keep a list of alternative doctors just in case. Use page 13 for your list.

Here are some questions you might ask your obstetrician. Add any personal questions that come to mind—and don't forget to keep a record of how they are answered.

QUESTIONS FOR YOUR OBSTETRICIAN
• Do you recommend childbirth classes?

• Do you have any advice on nutrition during pregnancy?

• What are your views on natural versus medicated childbirth?

• Do you encourage the presence and involvement of the father, other members of my family, or a friend?

• What procedures do you generally use for labor and delivery? What are the advantages and disadvantages of these? How flexible are you in working out an alternative plan?

• What percentage of your patients have Cesarean deliveries?

• How long can the baby stay with the mother after the delivery?

• If you are not available for the birth, who is your designated alternative? Can I meet him/her?

• What financial arrangements are acceptable? Will you bill in installments or in one payment after delivery? (Is this compatible with my insurance company's policies?) What does this fee cover? What is not covered by this fee?

• Add your own questions in the spaces below.

• _____

• _____

• _____

_____

_____

_____

_____

_____

_____

_____

_____

_____

_____

OBSTETRICIANS

DOCTOR'S NAME	ADDRESS/NUMBER	COMMENTS

✓ CHECKLIST
THIS MONTH YOU SHOULD:

☐ Find one or more suitable doctors.

☐ Interview the doctors and make a choice. Consider the options, i.e., midwife, clinic, home birth.

☐ Make the first appointment.

☐ Avoid X-rays and medication prescribed by a doctor who doesn't know you are pregnant.

☐ Read about your condition.

☐ Get extra rest. Pamper yourself. You're going to be someone's mother.

Add your own ideas below.

☐ _____

☐ _____

☐ _____

☐ _____

☐ _____

☐ _____

☐ _____

☐ _____

☐ _____

☐ _____

❋ NOTES AND OBSERVATIONS ❋

CHAPTER TWO

THE SECOND MONTH

PHYSICAL CHANGES

During the second month you may find yourself feeling extra tired. In fact you may find yourself falling asleep at the office, during dinner, on the train, or in the middle of a conversation. Do not attempt to fight this by drinking extra coffee (see page 24) or by forcing yourself to stay awake (if you can). Take all the extra sleep you can get, even if it means napping at lunchtime or going to bed right after dinner.

Don't feel guilty about sleeping. Your body uses the time to increase blood volume to nourish your baby. The extra sleep also prevents you from getting fatigued to the point where your resistance to colds and flu is lowered.

Another common change you may notice is a tendency to urinate more frequently. Your genital area may also be swollen and more sensitive.

PSYCHOLOGICAL CHANGES

The reality of anything is quite different from the expectation. Pregnancy can be more physically and psychologically shocking to your system than you expected.

Psychologically, there are so many things to worry about: Do I really want this baby and all the changes it will make in my life? Do I want a boy or a girl? Will I be happy with whatever I get? How will I know if my baby will be all right? Will I be a good mother?

The very fact that you worry means that you are already being a good mother. This is a form of stage fright. Some women experience it right up to the moment of birth. You can even have it with a second or third child. It's a way of talking yourself into a fine performance. Interpret it as well-founded maternal concern and learn everything you possibly can about the role you are going to play.

⚜ PRENATAL CARE

After some consideration you have chosen the perfect doctor. What can you expect of your first official visit?

This first visit is usually the longest. The doctor will ask many questions in order to get enough information to establish a personal medical profile for you. Be prepared to supply information about any family or personal illness and about your gynecological-obstetrical history. Questions about your race, religion, and age are asked because they may indicate a need for genetic counseling.

Another part of this and subsequent visits is the physical examination. A urine sample will be taken for analysis. You will be weighed so that your weight gain can be monitored. Your blood pressure will be measured. You may be given a Pap test if you have not had one recently.

The doctor will also give you an internal pelvic examination, and can usually tell from this if you are pregnant. Another test, the HCG test, is necessary before you can be completely sure. The HCG test measures hormone levels in your blood and gives results within twenty-four hours.

You may have a further series of blood tests that same day or when the results of the pregnancy test come back. Most of the tests are standard but some may vary slightly according to doctor and patient. These tests are performed for a variety of reasons:

- **blood count**—to find out if you are anemic.
- **blood type**—in case you need a transfusion.
- **RH factor**—to determine whether you are RH negative or RH positive. The RH factor is a blood characteristic. If the blood of both the mother and the father is the same—RH negative, or RH positive—there is generally no problem. But if the mother's blood is RH negative and the father's is RH positive, the baby may inherit the RH-positive blood and that may cause a problem. The mother's blood can produce antibodies to the foreign blood type of the baby and this is dangerous. It does not usually happen with the first child and it can be prevented from happening with further children by the use of RHOGAM, an immunizing substance that is injected within seventy-two hours after a birth, miscarriage, abortion, ectopic pregnancy, or amniocentesis. This is one of the reasons for being clear and accurate about your obstetrical history.
- **toxoplasmosis**—to determine whether you have immunity for this disease, a mild infection for you but quite damaging to the baby. Toxoplasmosis can be acquired by handling the cat box or by eating raw fish or meat. You may have become immune after a previous infection.
- **rubella, or German measles**—to determine whether you are immune. Rubella can cause severe physical handicaps in the baby.
- **venereal disease**—to determine the presence of syphilis, gonorrhea, chlamydia, or herpes infection.
- **sickle cell anemia**—an inherited blood disorder carried by about ten percent of Black and Hispanic Americans of African descent. Information about this and other inherited disorders can be obtained from your doctor or from:

The March of Dimes
Birth Defects Foundation
1275 Mamaroneck Avenue
White Plains, New York 10605

Be sure to discuss the results of these and any future tests with your doctor.

If congratulations are in order then you have subsequent doctors visits to consider.

Obstetrical visits are usually scheduled for once a month and include a weigh-in, urine analysis, blood pressure check, and physical examination. Toward the third trimester, visits accelerate to twice a month and then, when labor is near, to once a week.

In special cases visits will be more frequent. For example, a woman carrying twins or triplets will not usually carry to full term and will be seen more often. Note that it's never a good idea to schedule a business or social appointment for directly after your obstetrical visit. Babies are notoriously unconcerned about other people's schedules. If another patient needs your doctor's help during labor, it might alter your doctor's schedule, and make you late.

On the first visit you might be too preoccupied with your own hopes and wishes to notice them, but on subsequent visits take advantage of the maternity and baby magazines available in your doctor's office. They contain many helpful hints and descriptions of interesting experiences.

NUTRITION

Nutrition is one of the most important aspects of prenatal care. Medical experts used to believe that a baby would take whatever nutrients it needed from the mother's diet, however lacking that diet was. That turned out not only to be a false assumption but also a dangerous one. Your baby's mental and physical development will be largely influenced by what you eat. Not only do you have to eat for two—an extra 300–600 calories a day—but you have to eat wisely for two.

In the past, doctors advised women to gain as little weight as possible. Today, the proper weight gain is thought to be between twenty and thirty pounds. For a weight gain of twenty-four pounds the weight might be distributed as follows:

baby	8 lbs
placenta	1 lb
amniotic fluid	1½ lbs
breast weight gain	3 lbs
uterus weight gain	2½ lbs
stored fat, protein, water retention, and increased blood volume	8 lbs
Total Weight Gain	24 lbs

It's normal to gain two to four pounds in the first three months and a pound a week after that until birth, although the rate of weight gain can vary. A woman having twins will gain far more weight and at an accelerated rate.

You can expect to lose about half of this weight at birth and the other half three weeks to nine months later.

RECOMMENDED DAILY ALLOWANCES

Six meals a day are recommended during pregnancy. The March of Dimes recommends the following proportions of the following food groups:

milk and milk products: 4 servings
cheese, milk, cottage cheese, yogurt, powdered milk, vanilla pudding, ice cream

protein foods: 4 servings
eggs, kidney beans, pinto beans, garbanzos, tuna fish, salmon, nuts, peanut butter, fish, chicken, turkey, hamburger, lean beef

fruits and vegetables: 4 servings
citrus fruits, broccoli, chili peppers, leafy vegetables, bean sprouts, avocados, potatoes, carrots, snap beans, peas

grain products: 4 servings
pasta, rice, oats, grits, cornbread, tortillas, crepes, whole grain products

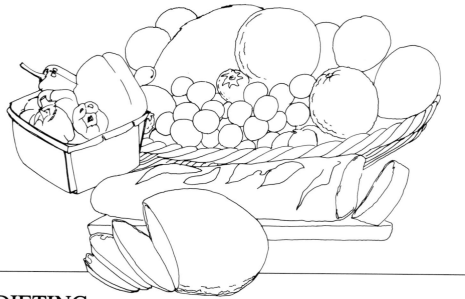

DIETING

This is not a good time to diet. Lack of the proper nutrients can harm your baby. Don't waste calories on chocolate and colas. They do nothing for your baby and make you unnecessarily fat. Instead of dieting, concentrate on making your calories count. Use the list of nutrient sources on page 21 and the recommended daily allowances with the sample menu on page 22 to balance your diet.

NAUSEA

Nausea is a special dietary problem of the first trimester. The rising hormonal levels during the first three months of pregnancy can make your sense of taste and of smell and your entire digestive system far more sensitive and temperamental.

Nausea is not a cause for concern or an indication of whether you are having a healthy pregnancy. Some women do not have any nausea. Other women have it from dawn to dusk for the entire first three months. Still other women experience nausea only after eating certain foods.

Notify your doctor if you are vomiting excessively, since this can lead to dehydration. Otherwise, don't worry. It's trying, but it will pass and you will have plenty of time later to catch up on your nutritional needs. Below are some proven aids to combating nausea:

- Try sipping fruit juices, peppermint tea, and soda water.
- Try eating dry crackers and protein foods.
- Never let your stomach get empty.
- Eat a cracker before you even get out of bed.

RECOMMENDED DAILY DIETARY ALLOWANCES FOR WOMEN

Based on figures supplied by the Food and Nutritional Board of the National Academy of Sciences/National Research Council—(Using Approximate Average Requirements)

	Women	Pregnant	Lactating
Protein	45 g	75 g	65 g
Vitamin A	800 mcg	1,000 mcg	1,200 mcg
Vitamin D	5 mcg	10 mcg	10 mcg
Vitamin E	8 mg	10 mg	11 mg
Vitamin C	60 mg	80 mg	100 mg
Thiamine	1.0 mg	1.4 mg	1.5 mg
Riboflavin	1.2 mg	1.5 mg	1.7 mg
Niacin	13 mg	15 mg	18 mg
Vitamin B_6	2.0 mg	2.6 mg	2.5 mg
Folacin	400 mcg	800 mcg	500 mcg
Vitamin B_{12}	3 mcg	4 mcg	4 mcg
Calcium	800 mg	1,200 mg	1,200 mg
Phosphorous	800 mg	1,200 mg	1,200 mg
Magnesium	300 mg	450 mg	450 mg
Iron	18 mg	*	*
Zinc	15 mg	20 mg	25 mg
Iodine	150 mcg	175 mcg	200 mcg

Key:
g = grams
mcg = micrograms
mg = milligrams

*The increased requirement of iron during pregnancy cannot be met by the iron content of typical American diets nor by the existing iron stores of many women; therefore the use of 30 to 60 mg of supplemental iron is recommended. Iron needs during lactation are not so different from those of the prepregnant woman but continued supplementation for a month or two after birth is advisable to replenish stores depleted by pregnancy.

NUTRIENT SOURCES

Here are some sources for the extra nutrients you will need:

Vitamin A—apricots, carrots, cantaloupe, broccoli, green peas, turnip greens, liver, peaches, papayas, bananas, oranges, butter, kale, winter squash, dandelion greens, prunes, mangos

Vitamin B$_6$—rice, bananas, oranges, corn, liver, meat, soybeans, sunflower seeds

Vitamin B$_{12}$—cheese, yogurt, fish

Vitamin C—avocados, potatoes, blackberries, blueberries, strawberries, brussels sprouts, broccoli, watermelon, kale, scallions, peppers, squash

Vitamin D—canned salmon, sardines, eggs, butter, liver

Vitamin E—almonds, peanuts, hazelnuts, cucumber, raw kale, vegetable oil, margarine

Calcium—milk products, sardines, turnip greens, nuts, legumes

Folacin—wheat germ, liver, nuts, beans, peas, whole grain cereals, orange juice, asparagus, broccoli, cauliflower, endive

Iodine—sea fish, iodized salt

Iron—beans, liver, an iron supplement

Magnesium—nuts, soybeans, lettuce, whole grains

Niacin—barley, wheat germ, rice, fish, chicken, sunflower seeds, peanuts, sesame seeds, split peas, pork

Phosphorous—barley, rice, wheat germ, cheese, yoghurt, nuts, peas

Riboflavin—whole grain and enriched breads and pastas, dark green vegetables, mushrooms

Thiamine—whole grain and enriched breads and pastas, peas, milk, eggs

Zinc—meat, liver, eggs, fish, nuts, wheat germ

DAILY DIET

Use this page to make up a diet of your own.

	MON.	TUES.	WED.	THURS.	FRI.	SAT.	SUN.
BREAKFAST	orange juice, bran flakes with peaches, milk						
MID-MORNING SNACK	peanut butter and jelly on whole wheat toast, glass of milk, pear						
LUNCH	glass of vegetable juice, egg salad on lettuce, two slices of pumpernickel bread, tomato slices						
MID-AFTERNOON SNACK	cup of yogurt, carrot sticks, glass of water or other beverage						
DINNER	chicken, carrot-raisin-apple salad, whole baked potato, green peas, glass of apple juice						
BEDTIME SNACK	crackers with cheese, glass of milk, dried apricots						
NOTES	*Sample diet courtesy of The March of Dimes						

DAILY DIET

Use this page to make up a diet of your own.

	MON.	TUES.	WED.	THURS.	FRI.	SAT.	SUN.
BREAKFAST							
MID-MORNING SNACK							
LUNCH							
MID-AFTERNOON SNACK							
DINNER							
BEDTIME SNACK							
NOTES							

NOTES OF CAUTION

There are certain substances that you should avoid during pregnancy:

CAFFEINE

Experiments using animals show that high doses of caffeine may cause birth defects and pregnancy complications. Try to avoid caffeine in large doses—keep it to 200 to 300 milligrams per day. According to the Food and Drug Administration, a five-ounce cup of coffee contains an average of 115 milligrams of caffeine, five ounces of brewed tea contains forty milligrams, five ounces of iced tea contains seventy milligrams. Sodas and diet sodas can contain as much as sixty milligrams of caffeine per twelve-ounce serving.

ALCOHOL

The Department of Health and Human Services advises, ''The more the mother drinks, the greater are the chances of health problems for a new born baby.'' Relatively small amounts of alcohol—as little as two drinks a day, twice a week—can cause problems. Instead of taking that drink, try to find new ways to relax. When you feel you want to drink something special or festive, try soda water or tonic water with lime or lemon, or fruit juices over ice with a fruit wedge.

SMOKING

Babies born to mothers who smoke have lower birth weights, more health problems later in life, and diminished mental capacity. The effects of your smoking during pregnancy last a lifetime. This is a good time to stop smoking.

YOUR MEDICINE CABINET

Take the following list to your medicine cabinet. Place a check after every medication you now use or might possibly use. Even if you only take a medication on a rare occasion, check it off and discuss it with your doctor *before* taking another dose.

- ☐ **Acne Medication**
- ☐ **Amphetamines/Diet Pills**
- ☐ **Antacids**
- ☐ **Antibiotics**
- ☐ **Antihistamines**—found in a variety of prescription and nonprescription cold remedies, cough remedies, allergy medicines and asthma medicines
- ☐ **Aspirin**
- ☐ **Birth Control Pills**—if you suspect that you are pregnant and you are still taking them
- ☐ **Laxatives**
- ☐ **Quinine**
- ☐ **Sleeping Pills**
- ☐ **Topical Ointments**
- ☐ **Tranquilizers**
- ☐ **Vitamins**

Add other items below.

☐ _____
☐ _____
☐ _____
☐ _____
☐ _____
☐ _____
☐ _____
☐ _____
☐ _____
☐ _____
☐ _____
☐ _____

ENVIRONMENTAL HAZARDS

Check your immediate environment—work and home—for any of these potentially harmful substances and make an effort to avoid them. If you have been or might be exposed, consult your doctor.

☐ **Asbestos**

☐ **Aerosol Spray**—in closed areas

☐ **Benzine**—including fumes

☐ **Bleaching Agent**

☐ **Carbon Monoxide**

☐ **Contact Cement**

☐ **Cats and Catboxes**—unless you have already had and have developed an immunity to toxoplasmosis

☐ **Dyes**

☐ **Fertilizer**

☐ **Fiberglass**

☐ **Glue**—not all glue

☐ **Hair Dye**

☐ **High Temperature**—including hot tubs and saunas

☐ **Herbicide**

☐ **Microwaves**

☐ **Mothballs**—including fumes

☐ **Oven Cleaner**

☐ **Paint**—including fumes

☐ **Paint Thinner and Solvent**—including fumes

☐ **Paint Stripper**—including fumes

☐ **Polyurethane**—including fumes

☐ **Radiation**—including X-rays

☐ **Sanding Dust**

✓ ## CHECKLIST
THIS MONTH YOU SHOULD:

☐ Have your first official doctor's visit and your pregnancy test. **CONGRATULATIONS!**

☐ Learn about pregnancy and nutrition. Begin to adapt your eating habits and make a plan.

☐ Cut down or eliminate caffeine in your diet.

☐ Cut down or eliminate alcohol in your diet.

☐ Cut down on or quit smoking.

☐ Check your medicine cabinet and discuss any medications with your doctor.

☐ Examine your environment and discuss any possible hazards with your doctor.

☐ Not overexert yourself; get plenty of sleep.

Add your own ideas below.

☐ _____

☐ _____

☐ _____

☐ _____

☐ _____

☐ _____

☐ _____

☐ _____

☐ _____

☐ _____

❧ NOTES AND OBSERVATIONS ❧

CHAPTER THREE

THE THIRD MONTH

PHYSICAL CHANGES

By the eighth week of your pregnancy your uterus has tripled in size. By the twelfth week it has started to swell your stomach upwards and you have begun to look the part of an expectant mother.

At about the twelfth week, the doctor uses the Doppler stethoscope to let you hear the baby's heartbeat. Don't worry—it's *supposed* to sound as fast as a speeding train.

Constipation, a problem for some mothers-to-be, can be treated by eating apricots, prunes, raw vegetables, and whole grain foods. Bladder and vaginal infections are quite common during pregnancy and can be safely treated by your doctor. Do not medicate yourself. By the end of the third month, you should be feeling a lot better and have more energy. Nausea and fatigue will definitely dissipate.

PSYCHOLOGICAL CHANGES

Many women report increased dreaming during pregnancy. This may reflect the increase in your hormonal activity, since frequent dreaming is often associated with other hormonal transitions. Women often dream of strange births and of difficulties with the developing child. These dreams are not omens, they are possibilities you are considering. Write them down so you can look at them some time in the future, when they may seem quite funny.

The first trimester is a very turned-inward time, especially if you are the sort of person who likes to think things over. The physical sensations of the first trimester are often impressive, and keep you focused on your body and the reason for the changes that are occurring. As these changes subside you will have more interest in the world around you.

⚜ THE HAPPY NEWS

One of the first things any expectant mother will do is share the news with her husband that he is going to be a father. The perfect setting is a dinner out or a special evening at home. Some husbands suspect they are fathers long before their wives do, so it may not be a surprise. Even so, it's nice to make a celebration out of so important and joyous an event.

Your husband will probably have one of the following reactions:

- delight
- pride
- surprise
- amazement
- confusion
- doubts
- all of the above

The balance in a couple's relationship changes with the impending arrival of a child. It changes what you both think about, how you spend your time together, who does which chores, and how you make and spend your money. Subjects never previously discussed (like whether to name the baby after your great-uncle) can cause arguments. It's a time to grow together, a time for patience and understanding.

Some men settle quickly into the reality of the situation, but others need time. Men wonder and worry about pregnancy just as women do. The only way to calm their fears is to discuss them together.

COMMON QUESTIONS AND ANSWERS FOR FATHERS

Q She's sick all of the time (during the first trimester). Is something wrong?

A Being sick in the first trimester is perfectly normal. It will pass.

Q Am I hurting her or the baby when we make love? Is it safe?

A Your doctor will discuss this. Unless there are complications, you can usually continue normal sexual activity. Sexual desire on the woman's part fluctuates throughout pregnancy. In *Human Sexual Response,* Masters and Johnson report that women's desire is generally low during the first trimester, when some women feel nauseous or tired. It is highest during the middle trimester and diminishes during the last trimester, when weight gain makes her feel cumbersome (you may have to experiment with new positions). Opinions differ about whether sex in the last trimester, particularly the last month, is advisable. Ask your doctor.

Q I don't seem so important to her anymore. All she talks about is the baby. Will she love the baby more than she loves me?

A It's natural for a woman to think, plan, and dream about her new baby. She will love it, but not in the same way she loves you. You will love this baby, too, and the one love will not diminish the other. It can even bring you closer together.

Q What kind of father will I be? I loved (or hated) my father. Will my child feel the same toward me?

A That's hard to say. Now is a good time to think about your relationship with your father, how it went wrong or right. Read some child psychology books. Talk to your father. Ask other fathers.

Q Will I be able to make enough money to support my family?

A It's been said, "Children bring their own fortune with them." Talk to friends and relatives to get a realistic picture of the day-to-day and month-to-month costs of child care. Realize that your income and life situation will change as the baby grows. Plan ways to save, stretch, or implement your income. Don't frighten yourself with a future you cannot accurately foretell.

Q It's a big commitment. What if I don't want to stay married? What if I don't like being a father?

A This is a tough question to answer, but once you're a father you can't stop being a father. There will always be a way to be the father your child needs, no matter what happens in the future. Plan for the best and work towards it.

SHARING A PREGNANCY

You two made this baby together. It will have some part of each of you, something that you can both look forward to discovering. Here are some ways to share this exciting time:

- Share information about how the baby is growing. There are some excellent books available that have pictures showing every detail.

- Plan a space in your home for the baby.

- Plan your birth method together. Plan the birthing. Attend birthing classes and practice the exercises together.

- Plan the clothing, toys, furniture, and so on that the baby will need.

- Choose the baby's name together.

- Attend visits to the obstetrician together. At the end of the third month you can both hear baby's heartbeat through the Doppler stethoscope.

- Share the birth. It's one of life's most dramatic events. Many men who were initially afraid to get involved in the birth of their child have been surprised to discover that they did not feel squeamish or out of place when they were at the birthing. Instead, they felt proud, important, deeply moved, and very close to the new child (it's much nicer than pacing the floor of the waiting room). Some fathers even cut the umbilical cord, and they get to hold the newborn baby right away—a wonderful treat! Many doctors and hospitals encourage the father's presence, even during deliveries involving forceps and Cesarean section.

PRACTICAL FATHERING

Your wife will not be able to do everything she did before she became pregnant. You might consider helping out in the following ways:

- If your wife becomes very tired during the first trimester, you might do the dinner dishes or share in the cooking.

- Carry heavy objects, like a week's worth of groceries or any boxes on moving day.

- Empty the cat box (unless your wife is already immune to toxoplasmosis).

- Refinish any baby furniture and paint the nursery (first read about environmental hazards on page 25).

- Take the older children to grandma's or to a neighbor's when the big day comes.

- Smuggle a picnic basket, flowers, and siblings into her hospital room.

- Arrange for baby/housework help for the first weeks, or help out yourself.

- Have the house tidy when she returns from the hospital so that she really can rest.

When you return to your office after the big event, don't be tempted to pass out cigars. Very few people smoke them, and the women in your office certainly don't. Try chocolates, cookies, flowers, or some inexpensive champagne.

If you have older children, bring them presents before the new baby comes home from the hospital. It's a nice association—babies are a kind of present, too.

EXPANDING A FAMILY

If you have older children or stepchildren, announcing the arrival of another child is not something you can do without first giving it some forethought. The ages of the other children can make a great difference in how and what you tell them.

Dr. Paula Ertel Feinstein, a child psychologist and mother of two, gives the following advice:

"You would not tell a two-year-old right away, not until there was some physical symptom that they noticed or until the last trimester. Don't expect them to accept it or to understand. If you say that you're going to have a baby, they think you're going to have a baby right now. They have no sense of nine months into the future. That's almost half of their life.

"When you do tell them, don't give them too much information about how the baby was born or made. It's not something they can understand. Also don't tell them that they will still be loved in the same way or anything like that, because this makes them think about a possibility they've never considered before. Say, 'We're going to be a family of four now. We loved having you so much that we decided to have another child.' Keep it really simple. If there's a reaction, comfort your child as best you can. Don't go into long-winded explanations.

"You might tell a four- or five-year-old before you tell other people so he wouldn't feel like he was the last one to know. You still wouldn't give him a sophisticated explanation. If he asked, you might show him a book with drawings on how baby grows, but not one with pictures because the growing baby looks bizarre to a young child. Kids at this age are busy differentiating reality and fantasy. If they were to see the fetus they would be likely to see it as a monster. Line drawings explain its growth. 'See how small it is and how it gets bigger.'

"By the time a child is ten or older he may see and learn anything he is interested in."

An older child may feel embarrassed by the evidence that his parents still "make babies" but they usually recover when the baby is born and are often quite interested in holding the baby and learning to take care of it. Some older children like to be included in the whole process, helping to plan and to choose a name. If they are that interested, they certainly should be allowed to help, because then the baby also becomes "their" baby. The guidelines for telling siblings are really very simple:

- Reassure them that you love them and that they make you happy.
- Make no promises for the future except the important one that they can discuss their feelings openly and honestly at any appropriate time before or after the baby comes.
- Answer any questions but avoid elaborations or unnecessary information.

You may want to make your announcement at a celebration dinner or small family party. Bake a cake. Make it a festive occasion. If your children see that the announcement makes everybody happy they will be more inclined to think of the arrival of the baby as a happy event.

EXERCISE

Exercise has many wonderful advantages during pregnancy. Exercise can:

- help you relax naturally
- improve your blood circulation
- give you energy
- improve your body tone
- give you self-confidence
- improve your posture and help you avoid lower-back pain
- help prepare you for labor
- help you regain your figure faster after baby is born

The first prerequisite to any exercise program is to consult your doctor, since some medical problems during pregnancy can make some exercises inadvisable. Exactly how much you exercise is determined by three general guidelines:

1. How much exercise you were doing before you became pregnant. Women marathon runners have actually won prizes while pregnant, but pregnancy is *not* a good time to begin running or even to begin training for a marathon. Remember also that if you already jog or participate in a strenuous sport, you must eat extra calories, especially extra carbohydrates.

2. Don't exert yourself to the point of fatigue. This means warming up slowly, even if it seems to take longer to warm up than it did before. It means that you must *stop when you feel any pain.*

3. Avoid exercise in which you are likely to have a serious fall. Even a small weight gain will alter your sense of balance. Your extra weight will also make you more susceptible to knee and joint injury in any sport that involves repeated shocks to the body (such as jogging on the pavement).

Most exercise programs adapted for pregnancy will include gentle stretching exercises, squatting and arching exercises, and breathing and relaxation techniques.

There are many excellent exercise books available, with illustrations and explanations. Buy one or more and practice at home. Fifteen or twenty minutes a day is enough to let you enjoy some of the benefits.

Joining an exercise class for mothers-to-be has the added advantage that you will meet other mothers-to-be in your area. Most maternity stores sell special exercise clothes that you will feel comfortable in.

Swimming is one of the preferred forms of exercise. Being underwater will make you feel buoyant and light even in your later months. Diving, scuba diving, and waterskiing are not good exercises for pregnant women.

If you're too nauseous to exercise in your first trimester, or just too busy, try a brisk walk. Walking has all the advantages of running—it's simple, free, and can be done almost anywhere.

If it takes you a while to get started on your exercise program, don't despair. You can start as late as your third trimester and it will still do you a lot of good.

MAGAZINE SUBSCRIPTIONS

There are a few magazines you can send away for. You will enjoy opening your mailbox and finding a magazine dedicated to just what you are thinking about. You can look through copies of these magazines in your obstetrician's or pediatrician's office and at some day-care centers. Some of these magazines will send you a free sample.

American Baby
575 Lexington Avenue
New York, NY 10022
☐ free except for special issues

Mothering
Mothering Publications
P.O. Box 8410
Santa Fe, NM 87504
☐ single issue $3.75; one year (four issues) $12;
☐ two years (eight issues) $22; three years (twelve issues) $30

Mothers Manual/Mothers Today
441 Lexington Avenue
New York, NY 10017
☐ two-year subscription, seven issues a year for $10

Parents
80 New Bridge Road
Bergenfield, NJ 07261
☐ one year (twelve issues) $18

Practical Parenting (newsletter)
18326B Minnetonka Boulevard
Wayzata, MN 55391
☐ one year (six issues) $7.50; two years (twelve issues) $14

Working Parents
Box 279
Bronxville, NY 10708
☐ two-year subscription, 6 issues a year for $10

✓ CHECKLIST
THIS MONTH YOU SHOULD:

☐ Have a small party to celebrate your pregnancy.

☐ Plan the months ahead with your husband. Spend some romantic time alone with him. Buy him a Father's Day present in advance.

☐ If you already have children, consider when and how you will tell them. Plan a fun activity you can do together.

☐ Work out an exercise program, even if it's just a brisk daily walk.

☐ Send away for free magazines.

☐ Keep a record of your dreams.

Add your own ideas below.

☐ _____

☐ _____

☐ _____

☐ _____

☐ _____

☐ _____

☐ _____

☐ _____

☐ _____

☐ _____

❧ Notes and Observations ❧

CHAPTER FOUR
THE FOURTH MONTH

PHYSICAL CHANGES

From the fourth month until a few days after birth, your breasts will produce a liquid called colostrum. Sometimes you may see a few drops and perhaps you will have to use pads inside your bra to absorb the moisture, or you may not notice any secretion until the colostrum is replaced by milk.

You may feel hungrier and thirstier this month, because your blood volume needs to increase. You'll be feeling better in general, less tired and far less nauseous.

During the fourth month your doctor may use ultrasound or amniocentesis to gauge the health of your baby.

PSYCHOLOGICAL CHANGES

Now that you feel so much better, your outlook on life is brighter. You look pregnant and will have the opportunity to talk baby with passing strangers. Your husband actually has physical evidence of your baby when he feels it move within you. In this way the baby becomes a reality for both of you.

This is a good time to start thinking practically. Do you want a bassinet or will you start off with a crib? What are you going to call this baby? Look around at baby paraphernalia. Make some baby-centered decisions.

The second trimester is a good time for most women, full of hope and good feelings about the future. It's time to have fun. Do things you enjoy before your weight and the last minute preparations encumber you.

❧MATERNITY CLOTHING

By the fourth month you'll find that a button undone here and there is no longer sufficient. If you want to look attractive and feel comfortable, particularly if you work and want to look as wellgroomed and professional as your colleagues, then it's time for some serious shopping. You may well wonder what to buy, when to buy it, and where to find it without spending a fortune. The answers to these questions are more questions.

First, consider your needs. If you work in an office or as a public representative you'll probably need more, and different, clothes than if your job is homemaking. Also consider which seasons you will be pregnant in. If you conceived in September, you'll have to think about an accommodating winter coat. Think about the rate at which you are expanding. If you are gaining weight at an average rate, you can manage with a mixture of wider-than-normal clothes and some standard maternity items. However, everyone will need certain basic items and they include:

Dresses—Choose styles that hang from the shoulder and don't restrict or pull on your new, fuller line. You can wear nonmaternity dresses but remember that they may pull up in front as you grow out.

Jumpers—These are even more versatile than dresses because you can mix and match them.

Maternity Shirts—Cut wider at the hem than regular shirts, these also often have detachable collars with frills and bows for a dressier look. Borrowing your husband's shirts or sweaters is also a way to add to your maternity wardrobe.

Jackets—If your job demands that you look your professional best, it might be a good idea to invest in one or two maternity blazers.

Pants—These are available with a variety of expanders. The most common style has an elastic front panel, but there are other styles with rib tops and rows of buttons that allow for growth.

Lingerie—You can wear any bra that offers good support but you may find that you have to change size once or twice during your pregnancy. If you plan to breastfeed, you will need to buy a nursing bra during your last months. Nursing bras either have snapped or hooked front panels that open for easy access, or the entire bra opens in front. Even if you have been able to wear your normal bra size for most of your pregnancy, buy nursing bras in a larger size. You can buy special maternity underpants, or you can continue to wear bikini underpants since these will fit under your stomach. Maternity tights are available if the queen-size or extra-large ones become uncomfortable.

Evening Clothes—Think subdued and pay extra attention to material and color. Avoid large prints or splashy accessories—you want people to focus on the details of what you are wearing rather than the expanse of what's under it.

Shoes—Buy flats because your balance will be altered by your new weight and your legs will tire easily.

Some women buy or sew an early-pregnancy wardrobe that they can wear again after the birth, while their figure is returning to normal. Simplicity Patterns has a wide range of maternity designs that are easy to put together even if you have never sewn before. If you are planning to breastfeed, remember that these clothes, as well as any nightwear you take to the hospital, should have front openings for easy-access nursing.

Make sketches of ideas and cut pictures from magazines and catalogues. Tape them to the note pages at the end of this chapter.

BEAUTY CARE

Renaissance painters preferred pregnant women as models because of their naturally rosy glow and their beatific expressions. The radiance of pregancy is not a myth and the best way to realize it is by taking the best possible care of yourself. Good diet, extra rest, and exercises will encourage the clear skin and shining hair that pregnant women are famous for and will help you make the most of this potentially beautiful time.

Your hair will seem thicker now, because the increasing hormonal influences slow down hair loss. Play this to your best advantage by having a good haircut. Keep it simple—a simple haircut, whether lightly layered or blunt cut, is flattering to your temporarily fuller figure.

Hair loss will increase again after birth due to a reversal in the same hormonal influences. Have your hair trimmed again and conditioned in the last month of your pregnancy so that you can look your best in the busy months after baby's arrival.

Hair dyes are currently being investigated by the FDA and are not recommended for expectant mothers. However, you can subtly and naturally alter your hair color with herbal rinses. For blonder hair, try camomile rinses and shampoos, and for red highlights and color, try henna preparations.

Your skin may be itchy during pregnancy, especially where it is stretching. After your bath dry off and massage into your stomach any of the following:

- apricot kernel oil
- cocoa butter
- coconut oil
- olive oil
- pure lanolin
- sesame oil
- wheat germ oil

To avoid staining your clothes, let these absorb into your skin and pat yourself dry before dressing. There is no proof that rubbing any of these into your stomach will prevent or diminish stretch marks but it can't hurt, it relieves itching, and it feels luxurious. Any stretch marks you do acquire will fade within a year to thin silverish streaks.

Beauty is not just in the eye of the beholder. It is also improved by the attitude of the beauty. Smile and enjoy the very temporary way you look. Take pictures of yourself in various stages and paste them in a scrapbook or on the note pages of this book.

STANDARD TESTS

Ultrasound is a device that uses high-frequency sound waves to locate and measure your baby and the baby's support system. After your stomach has been coated with a lubricating jelly or oil, a hand-held transducer, or sound generator, is rubbed across it. The sound waves create echoes, which appear as pictures on a small television screen that you can view. The image is wavering and fuzzy. Training is needed to interpret the pictures accurately but every now and then you will be able to see the outline of the baby's head or the movement of the body. You may even see the heart beat. It contracts like a small clenching fist.

A sonographer—a technician trained to read the fuzzy image—will measure the baby's head and limbs and see if the placenta is attached properly. Still photographs will be taken and you may even get to take one home for the family scrapbook. These pictures are not distinct enough, or so the doctors say, to see if the baby has mama's nose or daddy's chin, but it's interesting to save them for a later comparison.

Ultrasound is often used as a preliminary procedure for amniocentesis.

Amniocentesis involves drawing fluid from the amniotic sac, the fluid-filled balloonlike sack in which the baby floats. The doctor does this by inserting a needle through the mother's stomach and through the wall of the uterus.

This sounds more painful than it actually is. You may even have a shot of novocaine to dim the sensation of the entering needle.

The sample of fluid contains cast-off cells from your baby, and they are analyzed for genetic information. Over one hundred different defects can be detected by this procedure, and some can be treated while your baby is still in the uterus. Women who are likely to need this test are:

- those over 35, because a higher incidence of Down Syndrome babies might be born to them,
- those who have had one or more children with any defect,
- those who have been screened for, or suspect that they may be, carriers of genetic disorders.

You do not require hospitalization for this test, although you should rest afterwards and report any symptoms other than mild cramps to your doctor.

The test results are usually available in three to four weeks and you may, if you like, learn the sex of your baby. Amniocentesis has been a standard test for less than twenty years, and is an option your parents and grandparents did not have. Remember, however, that these tests are not required. There are some critics of amniocentesis and ultrasound who believe they are overused and promote an unnecessary sense of dependence on your doctor. You should discuss these tests with your doctor.

It's quite normal to worry about whether your baby is all right. Most mothers worry, although they won't always admit it. The odds of a woman having a healthy baby are ninety-five percent and that includes mothers with medical problems and poor nutrition. So relax. The odds are obviously in your favor.

For further inspiration you can try cutting pictures of beautiful babies out of magazines. Stick these on your bulletin board or on the note pages in this chapter.

✓ CHECKLIST
THIS MONTH YOU SHOULD:

☐ Collect maternity catalogues and plan a maternity wardrobe. Decide what you want to look like and what you want to spend.

☐ Get a flattering haircut.

☐ Buy some massage oil. You can add perfume to any of the oils mentioned on page 38 and give yourself luxurious rubs.

☐ Go out and have fun. Show off the new maternally beautiful you to the world.

Add your own ideas below.

☐ _____

☐ _____

☐ _____

☐ _____

☐ _____

☐ _____

Your informal wardrobe might include jumpers, shirts, skirts, and shorts. Choose easy to care for fabrics. Dry cleaning keeps clothes out of circulation for days and your wardrobe is already limited.

Pattern numbers (left to right) 6652, 6436, and 6252 reprinted by permission of Simplicity Pattern Co. Inc.

To look your professional best you might invest in a maternity blazer. Coordinate a subdued color scheme and use details such as bows, buttons, and collars to draw attention to your face.

Pattern numbers (left to right) 6652, 6252, and 6652 reprinted by permission of Simplicity Pattern Co. Inc.

Think seasonal! Will you be roundest in winter or summer? Will you need an accommodating coat or a swimsuit? Some early pregnancy clothes can be worn while you slim down in the months following the baby's birth.

Pattern numbers (left to right) 6251, 6436, and 6469 reprinted by permission of Simplicity Pattern Co. Inc.

❧ Notes and observationS ❧

CHAPTER FIVE

THE FIFTH MONTH

PHYSICAL CHANGES

A daily hour of rest can prevent fatigue and should be scheduled into every remaining day of your pregnancy. Even if you feel like you have energy to spare, some quiet time can be refreshing and very necessary to keep up your resistance.

You may want to nap for the hour or you might prefer to read, to listen to music, or to meditate. These are more easily accomplished at home, and resting during office hours will require some improvisation.

Your need for rest will increase as your pregnancy progresses. During the later months you should try to elevate your legs whenever you rest.

PSYCHOLOGICAL CHANGES

Birds make nests by gathering lint and twigs and feathers. Expectant human mothers display what's called "the nesting instinct" in many different ways.

Some women won't buy anything or make any final plans or choices until a few weeks before the baby's birth. Other women, influenced by family and ethnic traditions, will order everything to be delivered after the baby is born. Yet other mothers can be seen in the baby department holding tiny sweaters against their still-flat stomachs.

Different lifestyles and traditions influence the rate of preparation. It's nice if the nursery is finished down to the last detail but a baby is not loved less if he or she has to sleep in a lined cabinet drawer while waiting for the crib to arrive and the nursery paint to dry.

The most intense "nesting instinct" behavior usually happens a few days or hours before birth, when even the most casual housekeeper may find herself compulsively cleaning her house. This is as natural as birds fussing over their nest and it means that you're ready for your baby to arrive.

❧ THE BIRTH METHOD

It is never too early to think about the coming Birth Day, to learn what may happen, and to make plans for how you would like that day to be. If you have not already done so, this is a good time to select and register for childbirth classes. Classes usually begin in your seventh or eighth month and often consist of six to eight sessions, reinforced by at-home practice sessions.

You might also give thought to your partner in childbirth. Your husband is the natural candidate but if he cannot participate, you might consider a female friend or relative. In many countries a female assistant is considered an essential part of the birthing experience. Whoever does assist you should accompany you to all your classes.

The "prepared" or "natural childbirth" movement was pioneered by Grantly Dick-Read shortly after World War I and was publicized by his book *Childbirth Without Fear.* Dr. Dick-Read observed that not all women experienced pain in childbirth and concluded that pain felt in childbirth must result from a woman's negative associations with, ignorance about, or fear of the birth process. While every woman does have a different pain threshold, knowing what is happening to you, why it's happening, and what you can do about it will diminish the anxiety, reduce any discomfort, and help you feel in control. Preparation can make childbirth a more satisfying and even a pleasurable experience.

The Lamaze Method was named after a French obstetrician, Dr. Fernand Lamaze, and involves a process called psychoprophylaxis, which is the reconditioning of your reflexes. The Lamaze Method uses relaxation and breathing techniques that require a concentration that is sufficient to interrupt any signals that might be interpreted as pain. This method was introduced into the United States by Marjorie Karmel, author of *Thank You Dr. Lamaze.* Mrs. Karmel lived in France and gave birth to her first child with the help of Dr. Lamaze. Together with Elizabeth Bing, she founded the American Society for Psychoprophylaxis in Obstetrics (ASPO). Elizabeth Bing, a childbirth instructor and physical therapist, has written an excellent book on the Lamaze technique called *Six Practical Lessons For An Easier Childbirth.*

While the goal of these classes is a natural, unmedicated childbirth, the Lamaze Method is not incompatible with some forms of pain-relief medication.

The Bradley Method was named after Dr. Robert Bradley and concentrates on massage and relaxation techniques to tune you in to, rather than distract you from, the body's sensations during labor. His technique is also called Husband Coached Childbirth and depends on a good working relationship between husband and wife. His classes involve the husband in every aspect of the pregnancy and are usually taught by a husband and wife team.

There are other methods of preparation that employ variations of the same techniques. Since they are not as popular, it may not be as easy to find teachers in your area. Learn about all of your alternatives so that you can make an informed choice. See the Reading appendix under "Birth Preparation."

Some childbirth classes will discuss prenatal care, breastfeeding, and newborn baby care. Most classes will discuss birthing procedures, medications, possible complications, and emergency births. They may also show you a film of an actual birth. Since most women have never seen an actual birth, some women may find it disturbing. But the more films and pictures you see of babies being born, the less strange birth will seem and the more wonder and admiration you will feel about the whole birth process.

HOSPITAL PRACTICES AND PROCEDURES

Ninety-eight percent of babies born in America are born in hospitals. If you are planning a hospital birth and have not already requested a hospital tour, now is the time to do so. Familiarize yourself with the hospital layout, the best parking areas for admission day, and the area where admissions are processed. Some hospitals will let you take home an admission form and partially fill in information so you don't have to waste time being admitted when you are in labor.

While you are at the hospital be sure to ask questions about hospital procedures. Some of them may surprise you and are better thought about in advance. Procedures vary from hospital to hospital and many are elective. Some procedures are valid in emergency situations but are used unnecessarily in an uncomplicated birth. You should also stay current—hospital standards can change.

I asked Dr. Kathryn Schrotenboer, author of *The Woman Doctor's Guide to Pregnancy Over 35,* how she thought obstetrical attitudes and practices had changed in the nine years she has been practicing obstetrics. Dr. Schrotenboer said, "While there have been huge advances in technology, we now also have a more humanized approach to childbirth, since the patients, as consumers, have tended to be more verbal about what they wanted out of the birth experience and this has been integrated into the mainstream of hospital life.

"We now have birthing rooms. At New York Hospital we never do shaving or enemas unless they are requested. Across the country hospitals are looking at what used to be routine practices, such as episiotomies, standard birthing positions, whether or not your husband can be present, and whether or not your other children can see the baby right away, and are questioning their former attitudes."

In order to express your opinion, you have to inform yourself of your choices in planning the birth of your child. Some of the standard procedures you may encounter are discussed below.

Pubic Shave—Studies have shown that it does not reduce infection, as was originally thought. A miniprep or clipping is now sometimes done instead.

Enema—With better prenatal diet and exercise, this warm, soapy-water enema is not always necessary.

IV (Intravenous Injection)—A saline solution with five percent dextrose sugar is given routinely in some hospitals to every woman in labor. It is done to avoid dehydration and to counteract the changes in blood sugar levels caused by fasting during long labors or in women who have anesthesia. With an uncomplicated labor you may eat lightly and have fluids during your early stages and you will not need an IV. If you have been forewarned that you will need a Cesarian section or plan to ask for an anesthetic, you may not eat in early labor and you will need an IV.

Amniotomy—The doctor ruptures the amniotic sac to "speed up labor." In fact, labor is only shortened by an average of a half hour and can be made more difficult. The amniotic fluid protects the baby's head from undue uterine pressure. This procedure is not necessary in most cases and can result in complications.

Induction of Labor—This is done by adding the drug Pitocin to the IV. Pitocin is a concentration of oxytocin, the natural hormone that stimulates labor. Pitocin can make your contractions more painful and cause a decrease in your baby's oxygen supply. It has *not* proven more effective in stimulating labor. It *does* cause a higher rate of complicated deliveries and the need for anesthesia.

Fetal Monitoring—This procedure includes both external and internal tests. Externally, belts are placed on your abdomen that have monitors that read your baby's heartbeat. Internally, your amniotic sac is broken and an electrode is attached to the baby's scalp to measure the heartbeat; another device measures your uterine contractions. Discuss the use of these monitors with your doctor and make your own decision. Close observation, medical supervision, and listening to the baby's heartbeat through a stethoscope could reduce usage of these monitors.

Episiotomy—This is a surgical incision made to prevent tearing of the vaginal opening during the second stage of labor. It is performed in sixty percent of all deliveries. Many women deliver without tearing, and it is usually not necessary in second and subsequent deliveries since the area has already been stretched. It is necessary when your baby has to be delivered by forceps. Two ways to reduce the need for an episiotomy are by delivering in an upright position and by avoiding any anesthesia that interferes with normal pushing sensations.

Anesthetics—Those used to dull and diminish pain in childbirth may include ataractics, general anesthesia, narcotic analgesics, regional anesthesia, and sedatives. Write to the FDA and ASPO for literature on their side effects. Discuss these drugs and their advantages and disadvantages with your doctor. It's not a sign of failure or an admission of weakness to ask for or use anesthetics during childbirth. They are, however, not always necessary and they diminish your awareness of a unique experience.

Cesarean Incision—This is also called a C-Section. Instead of a vaginal delivery, the doctor makes an incision on your abdomen and removes the baby directly from the uterus. The incision may be done vertically or horizontally. The latter is called a "bikini cut" because it generally heals as a fine scar just below the bikini line.

Cesarean deliveries have saved the lives of many babies. This method of delivery has a definite advantage where there is a specific medical problem to consider. It is, however, done for many of the wrong reasons, such as a doctor's fear of malpractice suits, a lack of knowledge of complicated delivery techniques, and the inconvenience of a long or slow labor. In the last ten years, the incidence of Cesareans has risen from three percent to twenty percent of all births.

Delivery Room—During your hospital tour visit the labor and delivery rooms. In many hospitals it is still customary to move from the labor to the delivery room when you are about to deliver. This can be distracting and is usually only necessary in births where there are complications. Some hospitals now have birthing rooms where you can labor and deliver in the same bed. Birthing rooms afford more privacy and have a less sterile "operating room" atmosphere. In these rooms you are allowed to walk around and to choose birthing positions that feel comfortable to you.

Examination of the Baby—An extensive examination directly after birth by the hospital staff denies the mother and baby a chance to get acquainted. Behavioral psychologists and anthropologists claim that this is an important time for mothers, fathers, and siblings to meet with, touch, and look at the new baby. It certainly is an emotionally satisfying experience and adds to the mother's thrill of accomplishment. Dr. Frederick Leboyer has written a fascinating book called *Birth Without Violence,* in which he tells how a naturally newborn baby can be alert, responsive, and just happy to be born, if it is born into a friendly setting. Many hospitals now practice modified Leboyer delivery and attest to its virtues.

Ask that any extensive examination of your baby and the treatment that involves putting silver nitrate into its eyes be postponed until you have had a chance to spend some time together.

Can you refuse any of the standard hospital procedures? Technically, yes. You do not sign your rights away when you sign a hospital admission form. However, Dr. Schrotenboer advised that you should discuss these procedures and your feelings about them with your doctor prior to your delivery date. This will avoid any misunderstanding during the actual birth and will help create an atmosphere of cooperation and trust.

Draw up a birth plan and ask your doctor to initial it. Ask that it be attached to your hospital chart. Remember that this is an important event in your life. The doctor and hospital are there to ensure that you safely have the kind of birth you want. You may have to compromise on some points but if you feel too compromised to be comfortable or in control, change doctor and hospital. What makes changes in hospital practice is consumer pressure.

You may want to do some extra reading on fetal monitoring as critics argue that this procedure is an interference that may be harmful to your baby. Doctors claim that the monitors keep them informed of any stress or lack of oxygen.

"Hospitals are getting more and more amenable to changes," Dr. Schrotenboer added. "Hospitals need to make these changes to let patients get what they want and yet to have patients in the hospital for the one or two percent of cases that need emergency care. Hospitals need encouragement in making these changes and patients need encouragement in seeking this out in hospitals."

BIRTH PLAN CHECKLIST
Unless circumstances during labor make the following medically unsafe:

Patient's Request	Doctor's Okay
☐ I would/would not like a pubic shave.	_____
☐ I would/would not like an enema.	_____
☐ I would/would not like an IV.	_____
☐ I would/would not like an amniotomy.	_____
☐ I would/would not like the induction of labor by injections of Pitocin.	_____
☐ I would/would not like the following previously discussed medications:	
_____	_____
_____	_____
_____	_____
☐ I would/would not like external monitoring.	_____
☐ I would/would not like internal monitoring.	_____
☐ I would/would not like a Cesarean section.	_____

☐ I would/would not like an episiotomy. _____

☐ I would like my husband (friend, mother, coach)
    to be present for the whole delivery. _____

☐ I would like my husband (friend, mother, coach)
    to be present in the event of a Cesarean section. _____

☐ I would like to walk around during labor. _____

☐ I would like to take warm showers during labor. _____

☐ I would like to deliver upright. _____

☐ I would like to deliver in a birthing room. _____

TRAVEL PLANS

Travel plans for business or pleasure tend to get more complicated the further along you are in your pregnancy. Consider your travel arrangements well in advance. Consider making that trip now before your ever-accumulating weight and your impending due date interfere.

You may drive a car until you no longer fit behind the wheel, but don't squeeze yourself in. Should you suddenly have to stop the car, the forward propulsion would propel you into the wheel.

You may experience motion sickness during pregnancy but don't take any medication, including anything you usually take, without supervision. If you are planning a long car trip, either as a driver or as a passenger, be sure to pace yourself. Make frequent stops for short walks, small meals, and fresh air.

DRIVING

The Minnesota Department of Public Safety recommends the following tips for pregnant drivers:

- Wear your seat belt. Wear it low to pull in a downward direction on the pelvic bones. The belt should not pull back on your stomach bulge.
- Sit up straight, because slouching may cause the belt to ride up.
- Keep the satety belt snug, not tight, and wear your shoulder harness.
- Use the head rest to avoid body strain.
- Consult a doctor after even a minor accident.
- Avoid unnecessary driving.

If you have to travel to work by public transportation, try to arrange for an altered schedule at work. Ask if you can come in an hour late and leave an hour late. Avoiding rush hours can mean sitting for the length of your trip rather than standing. It also avoids the claustrophobia a pregnant woman can feel in a crowd.

FLYING

If you're planning a trip by air, keep in mind that some airlines will not take passengers past their sixth month of pregnancy. Other airlines insist that a woman be at least a month away from her due date and may request a medical certificate to prove it. The certificate will then be reviewed by their medical department.

It's a good idea to have a checkup before a long air trip. If you're traveling to a foreign country, ask your doctor for a referral to a doctor in that country. Since drug labeling and safety standards vary from country to country, avoid buying any foreign herbal remedies or over-the-counter medications even if they seem similar to something your doctor recommended at home. Ask your doctor about any vaccinations required, since some are the inadvisable during pregnancy.

• For comfort, choose an airplane, such as a 747, that has extra room between seats, or travel first class.

• Choose an aisle seat so you can get up easily and walk around at regular intervals.

• Wear your seat belt low, as you would in a car.

• Take naps and drink plenty of liquids.

• Don't rush yourself getting to the airport. Traveling is tiring for everyone but it's especially so when you're pregnant. Whether you travel for an hour or for a month, time spent planning beforehand will save you energy on your trip and ensure that you arrive at your destination in good spirits.

• Bring along or buy a sensible high-protein snack food, such as cheese (also a good idea when traveling with children).

✓ CHECKLIST

THIS MONTH YOU SHOULD:

☐ Read about prepared birth.

☐ Choose a partner for the birth and discuss preparations with him/her.

☐ Request referrals, and register, for childbirth classes.

☐ If you're planning a hospital birth, request a tour.

☐ Discuss birthing procedures with your doctor. Read enough to feel confident about any requests you have.

☐ Draw up a birth plan. Have your doctor initial it.

☐ Discuss your birth plan with your partner.

☐ Consider any travel arrangements you need to make during the remainder of your pregnancy.

☐ If you were considering a vacation, arrange to take it now.

Add your own ideas below.

☐ _____
☐ _____
☐ _____
☐ _____
☐ _____
☐ _____
☐ _____
☐ _____
☐ _____
☐ _____
☐ _____
☐ _____
☐ _____

NOTES AND OBSERVATIONS

CHAPTER SIX

THE SIXTH MONTH

PHYSICAL CHANGES

By the twenty-fourth week you may experience some physical complaints that are due to chemical and hormonal changes in your body and to the displacement of organs by your growing uterus.

Some women notice changes in complexion due to increased production of melanin, a skin chemical that darkens the skin. This increase can cause anything from darkened nipples and areolas to increased freckling, even to the "mask of pregnancy," darkened areas of facial skin. Some women also notice a "linea negra," or darkened line of skin that stretches from the pubic bone to the abdomen. These alterations in pigmentation fade after the baby is born. If you do develop a "mask of pregnancy" (also called chloasma), wear a straw hat in the summer and try to keep out of the sun.

Fluid retention may occur because one third of your weight gain is water. If you experience a swelling of your legs and feet, try to rest often with your legs elevated. In the summer months, when heat aggravates the problem, take frequent cooling showers and press cold washcloths to the pulse points at your wrists, temples, neck, and ankles.

If you are troubled by varicose veins, wear support stockings.

Gastrointestinal complaints are common and include heartburn, hemorrhoids, and constipation. They are due to a general slowdown in your digestive system caused by a decrease of the amount of the hormone progesterone. To relieve heartburn, eat slowly and chew spicy food well. Hemorrhoids can be soothed by taking warm baths and by applying cold witch hazel compresses. Constipation is helped by eating plenty of fresh fruits and vegetables, whole grain foods, and dried fruit, and by drinking plenty of water.

Backaches, another common complaint, are a result of poor posture made worse by your tendency to lean back in order to counter the weight you've gained in front. The strain is also aggravated by improper bending and lifting. Regular exercise helps. So does wearing flat shoes and squatting rather than bending to pick things up.

Some women have leg cramps. If you do, bend your foot upwards and massage the pain away. Drink milk for its calcium and sodium content and eat foods high in potassium. If the cramps are extreme or recur frequently, consult your doctor—you may need some nutrient and blood-count testing.

You will probably have some shortness of breath because your expanding uterus is pushing against your ribs and diaphragm. Pregnant woman also need more oxygen. So go slow, don't run to catch a bus or train, get your exercise, and *don't smoke.*

How women feel and what affects them during the later months of their pregnancy is influenced by their general health, body chemistry, and body type. A tall woman will not be bothered by some of the things that bother a short woman, for instance, and a woman in good health who exercises and eats soundly will not be bothered by problems that a less healthy woman might experience.

PSYCHOLOGICAL CHANGES

Music is an interesting aid during pregnancy because both mother and baby can enjoy it. Research has shown that unborn babies find Vivaldi and Mozart soothing but dislike Brahms and Beethoven (although the researchers never say which pieces were played). Researchers also say that unborn babies kick hard to the drumbeat of rock and roll, but it's hard to tell whether they are protesting or dancing.

Dancing around the living room to your favorite music is both fun and good exercise. You can also use quiet or moving music to relax or to meditate. Dr. Frederick Leboyer suggests singing as one of the best breathing exercises an expectant mother can do. It's good exercise both for your lungs and your spirit.

✦ PREPARING FOR BABY

It's never too early to think about baby's arrival. This chapter discusses some of the questions that come to mind as you begin to feel the baby move. Thinking about naming your baby, about your baby's physical surroundings, and the items baby will need in the first months is a good way to begin to establish a relationship with your baby—even before it is born.

A NAME, A NAME

Perhaps you are wondering what to name your baby.

"What's in a name?" Juliet declared. "A rose by any other name would smell as sweet."

A noble sentiment, but the lady in question was named Juliet Capulet and that's a lovely name. If she were named something really silly, it would be hard to imagine that she was so beautiful that she put the moon and stars to shame.

Images inspire sounds and sounds inspire images. Barbara is a bubbling, rolling, bantering, rhyming name because of the associations of its sounds. But the meaning of the sounds can be surprising. In its original Latin, Barbara means stranger, as in the root word barbarous. Maybe the ancient Romans thought barbarians bubbled, rolled, and bantered.

Cecielia, another beautiful name with beautiful sounds, means blind. Mary means bitterness, but thousands of Marys prefer to associate their name with the qualities of the biblical Mary.

The associations a name has are important. Obviously, you would probably prefer to avoid a name with a universally bad association, like Adolph, Judas, or Attila. Names are often temporarily favored or frowned upon because of news or media events. Beautiful names like Edith, Ethel, or Hazel have mediocre connotations because of their television associations, while equally beautiful names like Farrah or Vanessa seem all the more desirable because of the beautiful actresses who have them.

There are also personal associations. I chose what I thought was an unusual, lyrical name for my son and years later realized that it combined the sounds of the names of both my father and brother. These were pleasant sounds to me although at the time I couldn't explain why.

Should you give your child an unusual name? A name like no other can give your child strength of character and a sense of being unique but it can also provide a reason to feel separate and strange. Kids at school can make fun of even ordinary names, but if your child feels unjustifiably strangely named, his or her sensitivity will only encourage teasing. Research suggests that a child with a popular name will be more popular with classmates and teachers but there are also many happy and successful individuals who feel that their unusual name gave them a distinct advantage.

A name can be unusual in different ways and degrees. It can be a name from another time or place, a name you made up, or the unusual spelling of a popular name. It's up to you to weigh the pros and cons. Think about where you live and what kind of life you hope your child will have.

You also have a last name to reckon with. Consider your last name. Will your baby have your husband's last name, your last name, or a hyphenated version of both last names? Traditions are changing, but the laws governing naming vary from state to state, so check the laws in your area. How many syllables are there in your last name? If there are many I would advise you to keep the baby's first name short. Cornelius Frederick Oppenheimer is drawn out and seems old fashioned. Dennis Oppenheimer is easier to deal with and seems more modern. On the other hand, Joe Brown is not nearly as interesting as Ryan Everett Brown. Vary the length of the names, including any middle names, for poetic effect.

Consider the nickname people will make out of your child's name. If you like Robert but hate Bob, you might be able to insist he be called Robbie but you might also consider naming him Rob.

Watch out for strange initials. Peter Irwin Graves will become PIG. Mary Ursula Duncan will become MUD. Imagine these on a monogram.

In the space provided list five boy's names and five girl's names you like (unless you have had amniocentesis and already know your baby's sex). Look at these names for a few weeks, say them out loud and make sure you like the way they sound. Try to imagine babies with these names. Try to imagine first graders with these names meeting other first graders. Imagine teenagers with these names asking for their first date, receiving a school prize, or applying for a job.

Do they still sound good? Do the names sound right for a lifetime's usage? As parents your baby's name is your decision to make but you might want to ask your friends and family what they think (and you may be surprised).

Here are the twenty most popular names in the United States today and some of the meanings given for them in the *New Webster Encyclopedic Dictionary*:

- Amanda—loving, beloved
- Ashley—from the ash tree
- Elizabeth—worshipper of God

- Emily—industrious
- Jennifer—white wave
- Jessica—the Lord sees
- Lindsay—from the Linden tree
- Megan—great
- Nicole—victory of the people
- Sara—princess

- Adam—red earth
- Andrew—manly
- Brian, Bryan—strong
- Christopher—Christbearer
- James—supplanter, one who overthrows
- Jason—healer
- John—gift of God
- Joshua—the Lord is salvation
- Matthew—gift of the Lord
- Michael—who is like unto the Lord

NAMES FOR THE BABY

GIRL'S NAMES

FIRST NAME	MIDDLE NAME(S)	LAST NAME

BOY'S NAMES

FIRST NAME	MIDDLE NAME(S)	LAST NAME

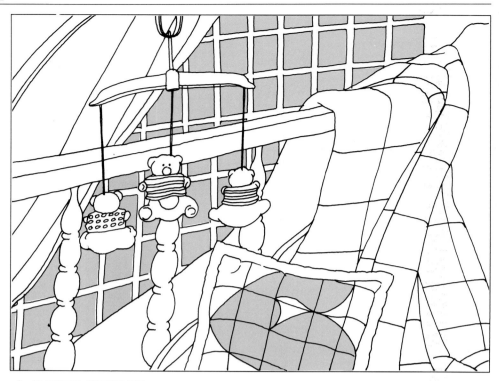

A NURSERY

A nursery needs to be well ventilated, well lit, and heated to at least 65° F. Nursery walls should be washable or wipable. Unleaded paint is the most practical wall covering, because small children love to peel off wallpaper, and cloth catches dust. Nursery floors should be smooth and washable. Rugs should be padded underneath or fastened to prevent slipping.

Planning a nursery is a pleasant task, and there are enough alternatives to suit any lifestyle. You may have a room you have been saving just for baby's arrival, or you may have to improvise. If you need to create a space, here are some suggestions:

- If you have a guest room, office, or dining room, convert this into baby's room. Use the attic, basement, hall area, or a closed-off porch for your guest room, office, or dining room.

- Divide your older child's room into two rooms by means of bookshelves or wall units.

- Screen off a corner of your living room or your bedroom to create space for the baby. Your bedroom is more practical, both for nighttime feedings and because its door closes out daytime noises.

- If you own your own apartment, maybe you can buy and incorporate an unoccupied next-door studio.

- If you have a loft, maybe you can rearrange and close off some space.

- You may eventually have to move to a larger apartment or house. Improvise until the baby is a few months old. It's easier to move with a baby than when you're still pregnant and tiring easily.

Wherever your nursery will be, it should be easily accessible. If you have a big house, use an intercom system that lets you hear the baby's reassuring snore wherever you are.

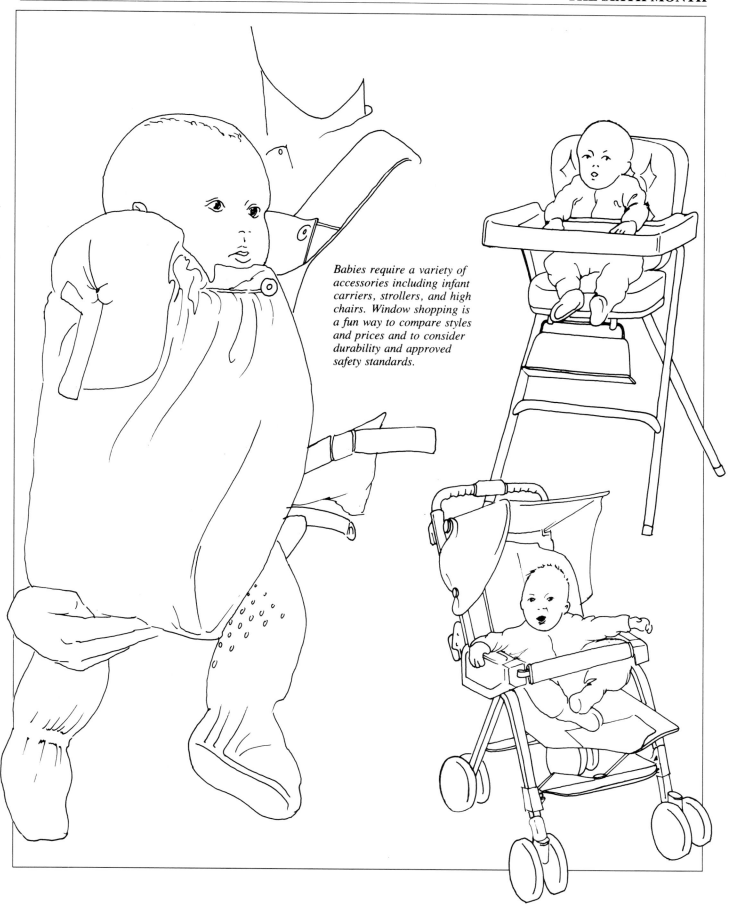

Babies require a variety of accessories including infant carriers, strollers, and high chairs. Window shopping is a fun way to compare styles and prices and to consider durability and approved safety standards.

COLOR SCHEMES AND THEMES

Choosing colors and patterns are part of creating a nursery that brings out the artist in every mother-to-be.

Soft, cool colors are tranquil. Warm, cheerful colors are reassuring and bright. Primary colors are stimulating. Psychologists and behaviorists say that babies enjoy being stimulated by bright colors, but how much they enjoy it will depend on the individual baby. A quiet baby will enjoy and need some stimulation. An alert and easily startled baby will need some calming down, especially when it's naptime. Your safest bet is to pick a softer color for your walls and floor coverings and to save patterns and brighter colors for your linens, curtains, and decorations. This also makes it easier to alter and adapt a nursery as the baby grows.

Any theme is possible. Sunny yellow is nice with wicker furniture and straw baskets for toys. Cool green is nice with plants, fish patterns, and an aquarium. Soft blue is brightened by rainbow rag rugs, rainbow mobiles, and bright window shades. Pale pink walls show off pink floral and Amish-style quilts, a collection of porcelain dolls, and framed children's book illustrations.

For decorations you can cut out magazine pictures and illustrations and frame them with inexpensive frames. You can mount posters, hang mobiles, stencil furniture, and pick toys all in the same theme.

Try to get your colors on paper before making a final choice. Get swatches of materials and paint samples and arrange them on the blank pages provided. (If you can't get swatches, take along a box of crayons and make appropriate matches.) When you find a winning combination, paste them in this book, label them, and take them along to compare other purchases.

NURSERY PARAPHERNALIA

The four basic necessities for any nursery are:

- Something for the baby to sleep in.
- Something for the baby to bathe in.
- A place to change the baby.
- Storage for the baby's clothes, toiletries, and accessories, and laundry.

How you arrange these and what you add to them depends on your budget, your imagination, and your sense of style. Here are some hints about basic comfort and safety:

Baby Bed—For the first two or three months, the baby can sleep in a cradle, a bassinet, or a large straw basket. These beds can be beautifully decorated and some mothers and doctors feel that babies are happier spending their first months in a snug, sheltered space. A disadvantage is that these smaller beds are relatively expensive considering their short period of use. For bedding you can buy specially fitted sheets, tuck crib-size sheets in folds under the mattress, or use diapers. A low Colonial rocking cradle or a Moses basket used first as a bed can be used later for storage.

You can also start off with a crib. This is a better investment since they last at least one year. The Consumer Product Safety Commission (CPSC) has regulated the manufacturer of cribs since 1974 and specifies that they adhere to the following regulations:

a) The height of the crib rails should be at least twenty-two inches above the mattress top when the mattress is at its lowest position. When the sides are lowered, they must be at least four inches above the top of the mattress.

b) The space between the slats can be no wider than two and three-eighths inches.

c) Metal hardware used on cribs must be smooth and have no hard edges.

d) Dropside locks and catches must be safe and secure from accidental release by the baby from inside the crib.

e) If you can put more than two fingers between the edge of the mattress and the crib, the mattress is too small.

The Consumer Product Safety Commission also recommends that you do not buy cribs with decorative cutout headboards, that you avoid decals because they peel off, and that you regularly check attached plastic teething rings since they break. Corner posts should not be higher than the crib's end panels. Check second-hand cribs carefully for these qualities, for lead paint, and for any wear and tear.

To protect the baby's head, put foam-and-cloth bumpers all round the sides of the crib. They should be tied in place with at least six strings.

Mattress levels adjust in most cribs so that you can use the highest level when the baby is smallest and lower the mattress as baby grows. When the baby can stand, it is a good idea to remove bumpers or anything else he or she could stand on to climb out of bed. Babies don't need pillows and should not have them until they graduate into toddler beds.

Distracting toys are fun for baby and might buy you a few minutes extra sleep. Buy or make a mobile and hang it over the baby's bed, but if it hangs low enough to grab make sure it meets toy safety standards (see Chapter Seven). Toys and activity boxes can also be attached to the crib rails.

Bathing and Changing Paraphernalia—For the first few weeks babies are sponged and not immersed in water. After the umbilical cord has fallen off you can wash them in a small plastic dishpan or a plastic molded bathtub. You can also wash your baby in the sink but watch out for hot faucets because the baby won't.

You can place the plastic bathtub on a dressing table, bureau, or tabletop, or even on a waterproof sheet on the floor. Once baby can sit up, you can place the plastic bathtub in the family tub or you can buy the baby a bath seat. Always support a newborn's head while bathing and *never, never* leave a baby of any age alone in the bathtub for even a minute.

After bathing, wrap the baby in a towel and lay him or her on a changing pad. You can change a baby on a changing table specially built for that purpose, with shelves and storage space below. You can also use a changing pad on a bed, table, or bureau, if you prefer not to acquire another piece of furniture. Another alternative is a changing tray that attaches to the side rails of your crib.

Never leave a baby alone on any raised surface. Babies learn to squirm at a fairly early age and in a minute can squirm themselves right over an edge.

Baby Storage—These problems can be solved in many ways. You can buy a set of baby furniture that converts into toddler/children's furniture for later use. You can also buy a crib with built-in storage drawers and shelves. You can buy a chest, dresser, or chifforobe in a thrift shop and refinish it. You can use baskets, shelving, or shelf space in an already existing closet.

For laundry you will need a diaper pail and a clothes hamper with a plastic lining.

That's it for essentials, but three other often-used baby items are playpens (or play yards), infant seats (or baby carriers), and high chairs. Playpens are not used in the first few weeks but it is a good idea to get the baby used to one during the first two months. Infant seats free your arms for other work and offer the baby a better view of the world. These seats may be used in the second or third month as the baby becomes more curious about the surroundings. High chairs are not normally used until the fifth or sixth month when the baby can sit alone but you may want to buy one as part of a nursery set.

The Juvenile Products Manufacturers Association (JPMA) carefully tests and certifies all baby products except cribs. They issue the followng precautions:

Playpens (or Play Yards) should have:

- no sharp edges, protrusions or points
- minimal potential for scissoring, shearing, or pinching injuries
- sides at least twenty inches high, measured from the floor
- holes and mesh openings designed not to catch fingers, toes or buttons
- locking devices that prevent the child from lowering or folding the play yard

Infant Seats (or Baby Carriers) should have:

- a wide, stable base with a securely attached supporting device,
- sturdy materials,
- bottom surfaces that do not skid,
- safety straps that should always be fastened when the baby is in the seat.

The JPMA also recommends that babies should never be left alone in a seat and that these seats should *never* be used as car seats.

High Chairs should have:

- a strong frame, joints, and seat that will withstand rough treatment from the baby
- a restraining device strong enough to keep the baby secured to the chair seat
- a tray that stays in position once it is locked
- proper balance and stability
- no exposed holes to catch tiny fingers and toes
- no sharp edges to cut the baby
- an easy-clean finish that won't peel or bubble

Some nursery additions that mothers will appreciate are:

- A rocking chair for those late-night feedings. Rocking baby to sleep eliminates, and is just as soothing as, walking baby to sleep.
- A bed or divan that can later be used as a junior bed. If the baby does not sleep in your bedroom, this bed can be useful for nursing or napping.
- A walkman and some tapes of your favorite music, also for those late-night feedings.

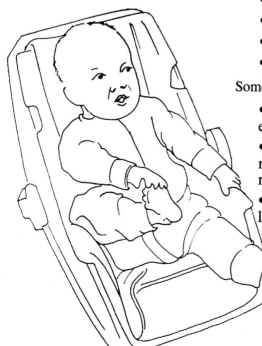

NURSERY COLOR SCHEMES AND THEMES

NURSERY SHOPPING CHECKLIST

Baby's nursery will need:

Decorating:

☐ paint or wallcovering

☐ curtains, blinds, or shades

☐ new flooring or rugs

☐ lighting

☐ mobiles

☐ activity boxes

☐ pictures and posters, etc.

Bed and Bedding:

☐ bassinet, cradle, or straw sleeping basket

☐ crib

☐ 6 bottom sheets, flat or fitted

☐ 6 top sheets (optional)

☐ 6 rubberized, flannelette-backed sheets, placed under cotton sheets to protect baby's mattress

☐ 12 diapers used as pads under baby's mouth and diaper area

☐ 5–6 cotton receiving or light summer blankets

☐ 5–6 winter blankets, quilts, or zippered sleeping bags

☐ bumpers for the crib

☐ ruffles and canopy frills (optional)

NOTE: Simplicity Patterns has a variety of patterns for baby bedding that include patterns for bumpers, bassinet lining, dust ruffles, and quilts.

Bathing and Changing:

☐ baby bath or small plastic dishtub

☐ changing table, plastic changing pad, or changing tray

☐ 2–3 soft terrycloth towels with or without hoods to wrap baby in apres bath

☐ 5–6 soft terry washcloths

☐ waterproof apron for yourself

☐ tray, basket, or shelf for toiletries

☐ mild soap

☐ a sponge

☐ cotton balls in a covered jar

☐ cotton swabs in a covered jar

☐ tearless shampoo

☐ baby brush and comb

☐ baby nail scissors (rounded edges)

☐ lotion or zinc ointment

☐ petroleum jelly

Storage:

☐ dressers, cabinets, or shelves for baby clothes

☐ hamper

☐ diaper pail

☐ garbage pail (that seals tightly)

Additional equipment you will need includes:

Baby Movers:

☐ a carriage

☐ a stroller

☐ baby carrier pack

☐ back carrier

☐ car seat

Miscellaneous:

☐ infant seat

☐ playpen (play yard)

☐ high chair

☐ baby intercom

☐ distractions and decorations:

☐ _____

☐ _____

☐ _____

☐ _____

☐ _____

☐ _____

☐ _____

☐ _____

☐ _____

BABY MOVERS

Babies love to move around. Not being able to is one of their earliest frustrations. From conception to birth they are rocked by their mother's body movements. Once your baby is born, you'll have to acquire one of the following to keep your child happily in motion:

- carriage
- stroller
- carrier pack
- back carrier
- car seat

Each of these is better for some situations than others. One or two will usually be enough. Think about your daily activities and decide which might fit in.

A carriage is best when you live on the ground floor (or in an elevator building) and you live near a nice park you like to walk in. It's difficult to get them up and down stairs and impossible to use them in public transportation. One nice feature of a carriage is that you don't need to move a baby who's fallen asleep during a walk. Carriages can double as sleeping space for the first three months.

A stroller is more practical. Strollers range from light "umbrella" models to heavier models that have a reclining backrest support that even a very young baby can sleep in. Strollers are easier to use on public transportation and easier to fit into a car trunk.

A carrier pack is one of history's oldest baby aids and one of the best baby buys on the market. Besides being helpful on outings, they are great at home. A baby feels most comfortable close to your heartbeat and body warmth. You can do many household chores with a baby tied into a carrier pack. Mothers of fretful babies swear by them.

A back carrier is sturdier and better for an older baby. It's very useful both for walking in the woods and for city shopping.

A car seat (for a newborn weighing up to twenty pounds) should be a tub-shaped bed that cradles the child in a semi-erect position. It should face the rear of the car and be secured to the seat by the adult belts already in the car. It should have a harness to strap the baby down, and for very small babies should be padded with blankets and towels on either side of the carrier.

These safety regulations were supplied by the JPMA (for carriages, strollers, and baby carriers) and by the National Highway Traffic Safety Administration (for car seats).

✔ CHECKLIST
THIS MONTH YOU SHOULD:

☐ Choose several baby names. Ask yourselves (and family and friends) how they sound.

☐ Think about where the baby will sleep.

☐ Use the shopping checklist to make a schedule of what you need to do and what you need to buy. If the baby is expected in April, you might want to paint in January, window shop in February, and make final decisions in March.

☐ Do comparative shopping. Note different prices around town. Investigate thrift shops. Ask friends what they might want to part with. Go to garage sales.

☐ Use the shopping checklist to calculate a rough figure for the total expense of equipping your nursery. Remember that you will get baby presents, so don't overbuy.

☐ Use music to make your last trimester more fun. Dance, sing, and entertain your baby and yourself.

Add your own ideas below.

☐ _____

☐ _____

☐ _____

☐ _____

☐ _____

❈ NOTES AND OBSERVATIONS ❈

CHAPTER SEVEN

THE SEVENTH MONTH

PHYSICAL CHANGES

Even though the average weight gain is between twenty-four and twenty-eight pounds, don't be tempted to diet if you already reach this weight by the seventh or eighth month. During the last trimester your baby still has a lot of important growing to do so be patient with your bulkiness and continue to eat sensible, nutrient rich foods. Baby's weight triples during the last months from two to seven or more pounds. His movements, which were first felt as a soft flutter, are now visible acrobatics that extend and ripple the surface of your abdomen. These movements are reassuring and exciting since they make baby and his impending arrival seem all the more real.

PSYCHOLOGICAL CHANGES

While it is no longer believed that a single experience during pregnancy can make an indelible impression on a baby, it is true that an expectant mother's general emotional atmosphere can affect her child's behavior. Everyone laughs when a comedian says, "I look like this because when my mother was pregnant, she was scared by a . . ." Yet when a mother is under stress, her heart does accelerate, her body pumps extra adrenaline, and her vitamin and mineral absorption are interfered with, all of which affects her baby. Babies born to mothers who underwent prolonged periods of stress were found to cry more easily, startle more easily, and have more feeding problems.

Try to avoid stress. Try to avoid excessive noise, overly crowded situations, and sudden shocks. Try also to avoid overcrowding your time.

Do take time for long walks in lovely settings and trips to museums and galleries. They'll make you feel good and positive about life. Spend time with your favorite people and in pleasant, relaxing environments.

Relax and enjoy the positive aspects of your pregnancy. Imagine your baby with all the qualities you are wishing for. Laugh a lot—this massages your baby.

⚜ A LAYETTE

Newborn clothes are available in a rainbow of soft colors and a variety of multi-purpose styles. It's natural to want your baby to be beautifully dressed and it's fun to shop for, to inherit, or to make such tiny clothes. Use the Layette Checklist for shopping convenience and remember that:

- Newborns dislike being completely undressed. Kimonos and night-gowns are practical for the first few months because they do not have to be removed when you change the baby's diapers. Cuffs at the sleeves prevent the baby from accidentally scratching him or herself.

- Babies dislike anything that stretches over their heads. Choose loose or snap collars or clothes that button down. Avoid drawstrings at the neck.

- Your baby may outgrow most of the original wardrobe within six weeks. Consider buying or making some extra items in the next larger size.

- Judge clothing sizes by the pounds mentioned on the sizing labels rather than by the months. Every baby gains weight at a different rate.

- New parents are surprised at the volume of laundry a newborn can generate. If you do not own your own washing machine, buy extra of everything washable.

ILLUSTRATIONS OF BABY CLOTHES

Clip and paste pictures of those you especially like.

ILLUSTRATIONS OF BABY CLOTHES

Clip and paste pictures of those you especially like.

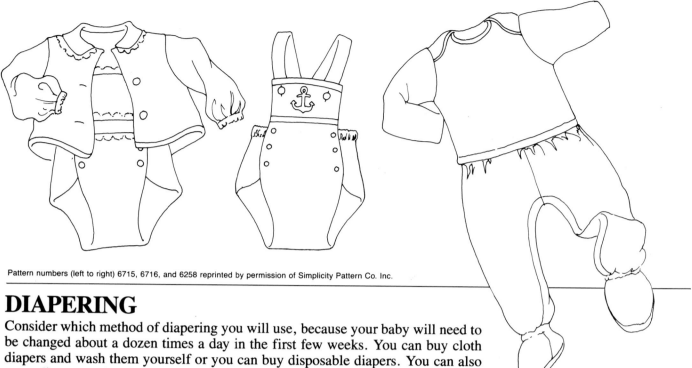

Pattern numbers (left to right) 6715, 6716, and 6258 reprinted by permission of Simplicity Pattern Co. Inc.

DIAPERING

Consider which method of diapering you will use, because your baby will need to be changed about a dozen times a day in the first few weeks. You can buy cloth diapers and wash them yourself or you can buy disposable diapers. You can also use a diaper service that delivers clean diapers once a week.

Consider what's involved. Check on the cost of a few diaper services in your area, and compare the price of disposables. Calculate the time it will take you to wash and dry your own cloth diapers. Many parents use a combination of diapering methods. They may use a service for the first few weeks. Then they may switch to disposables during the day and use cloth diapers at night when the baby has to go longer stretches without being changed. You have to decide which method is most time and cost-efficient for you.

Babies who only wear disposables have a higher incidence of diaper rash. Babies catered to by a diaper service have the least. Every baby will have some diaper rash but here are some tips for avoiding a serious episode:

- Change the baby often.
- Wash the baby with warm water and mild soap at every changing, rinsing thoroughly and patting dry.
- Apply a barrier cream or ointment at every diapering.
- Leave the baby without a diaper when possible, especially when there is already some rash.
- When washing diapers, use a mild soap. Disinfect them with bleach or diaper antiseptic. Do not use fabric softener, and rinse bleached diapers at least twice in cold water.
- Dry in sunlight if possible.
- Some babies are allergic to some formula, cow's milk, or synthetic vitamin drops, and these may cause an allergic reaction.
- Use thicker diapering at night.
- Consult your pediatrician if the rash gets very red, raw, or blistery.

Use the Layette Checklist for determining quantities.

TWO WAYS TO FOLD A DIAPER

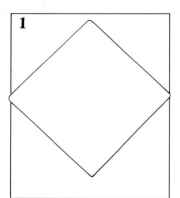

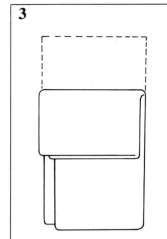

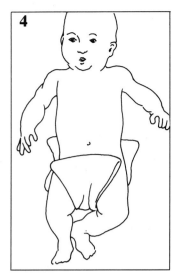

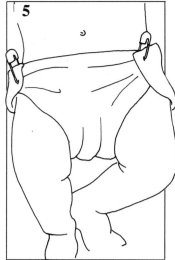

1. Fold diaper vertically in half.

2. Fold up one third of diaper horizontally.

3. Lay baby on diaper so that top edge is at the middle of his back.

4. Fold up folded third of diaper to baby's waist.

5. Attach outer edges of bottom to front part of diaper with a safety pin on either side.

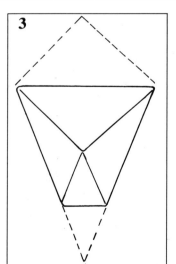

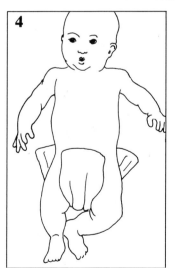

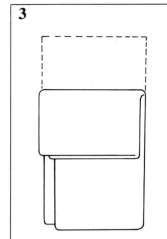

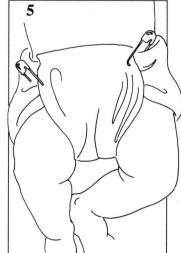

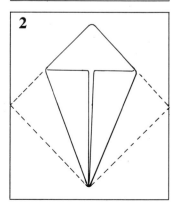

1. Fold two outer points of diaper towards each other.

2. Fold top flap down to where those points meet.

3. Fold bottom point to where the other points meet.

4. Lay baby on diaper so that the top edge is at the middle of his back.

5. Fold the lower and thickest flap up to his waist. Tie both edges of lower part with safety pins. (Tie them together with one when baby is small and at either side of front part with two safety pins when baby is larger.)

LAYETTE CHECKLIST

Basic Clothes:

		NOTES
☐ nightgowns	2–3	_____
☐ kimonos	2–3	_____
☐ stretch terrycloth coveralls	4–6	_____
☐ cotton t-shirts	6	_____
☐ socks	3–4 pairs	_____
☐ bibs	optional	_____

Summer Clothes:

☐ light sweaters	2	_____
☐ cotton shawls or receiving blankets	2–3	_____
☐ summer hat for shade	2	_____

Winter Clothes:

☐ sweaters and leggings	4–5	_____
☐ bunting and/or a snow suit	1–2	_____
☐ winter hats	2	_____
☐ booties	2 pairs	_____
☐ mittens	2 pairs	_____

Diapers:

☐ if you are washing your own diapers	4–6 dozen	_____
☐ if you are using a diaper service	2–4 dozen	_____
☐ if you are using disposables, the approximate first month use	300 +	_____

Diaper Accessories:

☐ waterproof plastic pants for use with cloth diapers	4–6	_____
☐ terrycloth pants for wearing over disposables	4–6	_____
☐ diaper liners for wearing in cloth diapers	1 box	_____
☐ diaper pins	1 dozen	_____

Miscellaneous:

☐ _____

☐ _____

☐ _____

☐ _____

PLAYTHINGS

Toys are a fun way for babies to learn about the world they live in. Always try to choose playthings suitable to your child's age. During the first three months, toys should help the baby to focus attention on what he or she sees and hears, and to explore the way things look, sound, and feel. Toys that do not have to be held are best. Some good ones are:

- mobiles
- wind chimes (well out of baby's reach)
- musical crib toys
- musical stuffed animals
- squeeze and squeak puppets
- wrist rattles

From three to six months, a child's grasp improves, and your baby will be eager to discover different textures and shapes. Your baby will also become more aware of being separate from other people. All babies love to look at faces whether they are those of other people, in pictures, toy faces or their own mirrored image. Toys that a three- to six-month-old will appreciate are:

- activity boxes
- rattles
- wheeled cars
- easy-to-squeeze toys
- bathtime toys
- mirrors (edges must be smooth and framed and the mirrored surface made of polished metal)

The government issues safety regulations concerning toy manufacture. The Consumer Product Safety Commission and the Toy Manufacturers of America, Inc. both offer guidelines for toy purchasing and maintenance safety.

The Toy Manufacturers of America, Inc. suggest that for children younger than eighteen months old, playthings should be:

- too large to swallow
- lightweight for handling and grasping
- free of sharp points or edges
- brightly colored
- nontoxic

The Consumer Product Safety Commission has the following suggestions for toy safety:

- Look for labels recommending suitable age. A toy that is safe for an eight-year-old may be hazardous for a younger child.
- Avoid hand-me-down toys with small parts until children are over three years of age.
- Avoid toys with long strings or cords. Never use long strings, cords, loops, or ribbons to hang toys in cribs or playpens, because children can easily become entangled.
- Examine toys periodically. Repair broken toys and discard toys that cannot be fixed.

TOY CHESTS

Toy chests are sometimes bought as part of a nursery set. If you use a chest with a lid, the Consumer Product Safety Commission recommends that you get one with a hinge that will hold the lid open in any position. Test it to see that the hinge does in fact prevent the lid from falling. If you inherit a toy chest or buy a used one that has a falling lid, install a lid-support device. Check this device periodically to see that it still works.

You might consider buying a chest with sliding or panel doors, one with a lightweight lid, or simply an open chest or toy box. For extra safety choose one with rounded or padded edges and corners.

A toy chest can be both decorative and functional. As soon as the baby can sit, you can begin to teach lessons about putting toys into the chest. Most babies enjoy that first lesson in room tidying.

BREAST VS. BOTTLE

In order to know what feeding equipment you must buy, you will have to give some thought as to whether you want to breastfeed or bottle-feed your baby. Here are some interesting facts and hints on breastfeeding.

- Babies receive valuable antibodies from the mother's milk.

- Breast milk is convenient and always the right temperature. No time is spent making formula or sterilizing bottles. When breastfeeding you do need extra rest, extra fluids, extra calories, and a vitamin supplement.

- Breast milk is easily digested. Cow's milk can cause an allergic reaction. Breastfed babies spit up less, have less diaper rash, and less constipation.

- The supply of breast milk is regulated by demand. Breastfed babies are rarely overweight.

- The size and shape of your breasts do not affect your ability to breastfeed. Neither does breastfeeding permanently alter the shape of your breasts.

- A baby should be put to the breast in the delivery room to help shrink the uterus and to help deliver the placenta. Colostrum, the white thickish breast fluid secreted during the first seventy-two hours, helps prepare the baby's digestive system for milk.

- To help the baby find your breast, stroke the baby's cheek nearest your breast and the baby will turn toward it.

- If your milk is coming too fast for your baby, hold the nipple away with your fingers.

- It usually takes about five to ten minutes to empty each breast, although some babies love to nurse and linger.

- A baby with a stuffy nose will not want to nurse. Use a nasal aspirator or ask your pediatrician to recommend nose drops.

- If you have to work or be away from your baby for a long time, you can use a breast pump to draw out milk and save it for the feeding when you won't be there, or you can try alternating breast milk and formula feedings.

- The following substances taken by the mother will find their way into your breast milk: alcohol, antibiotics, aspirin, bromides, caffeine, iodine, laxatives, nicotine, opiates, tranquilizers, vitamin C. Discuss the use of these and any other medications with your doctor.

Breastfeeding is generally a very pleasant experience. Relax and enjoy it. Look at your baby, because your baby will be looking at you, trying to discover everything about you.

How long you continue to breastfeed depends on how much you enjoy it and how long it is convenient. Some babies lose interest in breast milk when they begin solid foods. Some mothers lose interest in breastfeeding when they decide to go back to work or when the baby develops teeth.

Here are some facts and hints about bottle-feeding:

- One definite advantage of bottle-feeding is that you can leave the baby in the care of a nurse or babysitter.

• The father can participate in the baby's care and help with late-night feedings.

• In the first months you may have to sterilize your equipment twice a day. There are two methods of sterilization. One involves sterilizing all of your equipment and adding the formula. The other involves sterilizing formula and bottles at the same time. The sterilizing unit you buy will have instructions enclosed.

• Ask your future pediatrician (see Chapter Eight) to recommend a formula.

• When preparing bottles, always check to see how the nipple is flowing. Test the milk temperature by splashing it against your wrist. It should not be noticeably warm or cold.

• If you cuddle and hold your baby close during the feeding, your bottle-fed baby will feel just as loved and cherished as a breastfed baby.

✓ CHECKLIST
THIS MONTH YOU SHOULD:

☐ Plan a schedule for acquiring baby clothes. Do some comparative shopping, noting prices on the Layette Checklist. Look at baby-clothes patterns (Simplicity has many).

☐ Consider which method of diapering you'll use. Price disposables, cloth diapers, and diaper services.

☐ Get at least one cloth diaper and practice different diapering techniques.

☐ Consider your laundry situation. Maybe it's time to get a washing machine.

☐ Will you breast or bottle feed? Ask friends and read books about that part of the mothering experience. The La Leche League will answer any questions you have. (See the Reading appendix under "Breastfeeding Basics").

☐ If you bottle-feed, familiarize yourself with the sterilizing procedures. Do at least one trial sterilization before you bring the baby home.

☐ If you bottle-feed, you will need the following equipment:

    ☐ nine or ten 8-ounce bottles

    ☐ one dozen nipples

    ☐ a sterilizing unit

    ☐ stirring spoons with long handles

    ☐ measuring spoons

    ☐ tongs

    ☐ a bottle brush

    ☐ a nipple brush

    ☐ can opener

    ☐ formula

    ☐ bottle warmer (optional)

☐Plan some relaxing outings for you and your husband. Things tend to get more hectic in the last trimester, and you'll both need a break now and then.

Add your own ideas below.

☐_____

☐_____

☐_____

☐_____

☐_____

☐_____

☐_____

☐_____

☐_____

☐_____

☐_____

☐_____

☐_____

☐_____

❧ NOTES AND OBSERVATIONS ❧

CHAPTER EIGHT

THE EIGHTH MONTH

PHYSICAL CHANGES

Now is the time to increase your daily rest period to two hours (see Physical Changes, Chapter Five), preferably with your legs elevated. If this is difficult at work, do it once you arrive home. Besides the strain of carrying extra weight around with you, you may also be getting less sleep because of the baby's increasingly noticeable nighttime activity. It's a mistake to go into labor exhausted, so remember to pace yourself well. This is an ideal time to begin your maternity leave.

PSYCHOLOGICAL CHANGES

The approach of your delivery date can reawaken some of your earlier anxieties. First-time mothers wonder what labor will be like, if they will feel pain and if so, whether they will be able to handle it. They wonder if they will be good mothers. They wonder what their babies will be like. It's important to remember that very little about children is predictable—and that starts from the day they are born.

You have done everything you could to have a safe and enjoyable birth but you may have some problems just the same. For instance, despite the success of Lamaze techniques, women can experience varying degrees of pain. Some women's labor contractions suddenly stop. Some labors are long and complicated.

Asking for medication does not mean you have failed (but be sure you have educated yourself about the options). Many mothers feel they have failed if they have to have a medicated or a Cesarean birth. A woman who has strong feelings about these matters would be wise to discuss them with her doctor, her husband, and other friends. Childbirth is not a competition or a race for a merit badge, and the best of planning and intent cannot guarantee predictable results.

Your baby may not look anything like you expected or be the sex you hoped for. You may not get to hold the baby right away or even fall in love at once. Just remember that you have a lifetime to care for your child. By the time you see that first little smile you will love your baby. Any little disappointments will be forgotten.

Plan and hope for the best and remember that every birth and every child is unique.

❧ A SHOWER

You may be the lucky recipient of a baby shower. Traditionally, these are given a month before your due date but they may also be given after the baby is born. Showers used to be held in the afternoon with light, tea-time refreshments served and only female friends and relatives invited. Many showers today have both male and female guests and are given in the evening.

A typical office shower consists of the entire office staff taking the mother-to-be out to lunch and contributing to a communal present.

The arrangements for a shower are the responsibility of your hostess, but she may ask you to supply a list of names of those you would like to invite. She will also ask you to give her a list of whatever baby essentials you need so that she can coordinate the purchasing of presents.

Once you have taken out your address book to compile that list, you can start to think about who you would like to send birth announcements to. It is polite to send a thank-you note to everyone who has given you a present, even if you have already thanked them in person. The thank-you note can be included with (and on paper matching) your birth announcement. Keep notes on what each person gives you so you can personalize your thank-you notes. It's rewarding to the giver to hear that the pink quilt fits perfectly into the color scheme of the baby's room or that the blue sweater is exactly right.

SHOWER GUEST LIST

Date _____ Time _____

Location _____ Phone _____

Hostess _____

Guest's Name	Address	Phone
1.		
2.		
3.		
4.		
5.		
6.		
7.		
8.		
9.		

SHOWER GUEST LIST

Date _____ Time _____

Location _____ Phone _____

Hostess _____

Guest's Name   Address   Phone

10. _____

11. _____

12. _____

13. _____

14. _____

15. _____

16. _____

17. _____

18. _____

19. _____

20. _____

21. _____

22. _____

23. _____

24. _____

25. _____

26. _____

27. _____

28. _____

29. _____

AN ANNOUNCEMENT

A birth announcement is an excellent way to share the happy event with family and friends, far and near. This welcome addition to their daily mail can be sent in a variety of styles and formats.

The most traditional announcement consists of two cards. The larger card simply states the parents' names and address. A smaller or "baby" card will be attached to this card with a pink or a blue ribbon and will contain the baby's name and birth date.

Another traditional announcement states all of the information on the same card, using a variation of the same joyful theme:

> Mr. and Mrs. John Brown
> have the pleasure of announcing
> the birth of a daughter,
> Abigail Jean,
> on March 25, 1988

Instead of Mr. and Mrs. J. Brown you might also say John and Mary Brown. If you have kept your maiden name after your marriage, it might read:

John and Mary Smith Brown
joyfully announce . . .

If you already have other children and would like to include them, you have three basic options. You can say, "John, Mary, George, and Sally Brown are pleased to announce . . ." or you can say, "John and Mary Brown and their children, George and Sally, are delighted to announce. . . ." You could also say:

> John, Mary, George, and Sally Brown
> are happy to announce
> the birth of a daughter and sister,
> Abigail Jean. . . .

The stationery sections of some department stores will allow you to take envelopes home in advance when you come in to choose the design and typeface of your announcement. This enables you to address and stamp the envelopes at your leisure. After the birth, you can call in the baby's vital statistics. Your order, with or without matching thank-you notes, will be printed in three or four weeks after you supply the necessary information.

If you choose to go to a stationer, you can write your own wording for the announcement. You might say:

> *Our wonderful daughter, Abigail Jean,*
> *arrived early on a spring morning . . . .*

You can start composing original declarations now or you can choose an appropriate saying that appeals to you. For example:

> *"There was a star danced and under that was I born."*
> *(William Shakespeare)*

> *"Children are a gift from God."*
> *(Psalms 127:3)*

You can also preview designs and typefaces at a printer/stationer but you may have to make another visit to finalize the order. Printing can take anywhere from one to four weeks and you may have to wait for your envelopes. Minimum quantities and prices vary, so make comparisons.

There are hand-crafted and personalized cards available by mail order. Look for advertisements in baby magazines. You can also buy some lovely, preprinted packaged cards in stationery stores and fill out your own information. These can also be pre-addressed, stamped, and filled out in the hospital so that everyone can be notified immediately. An advantage to mailing announcements four to six weeks after the birth is that by then you will have accumulated presents, a thank-you list, and possibly some photographs.

Don't forget to send an announcement to your obstetrician. Some doctors proudly display bulletin boards full of the snapshots and statistics of newborns.

Save one announcement to frame or paste in the baby's scrapbook.

ANNOUNCEMENT/THANK-YOU LIST

NAME	ADDRESS	PRESENT	THANK-YOU NOTE SENT
1.			
2.			
3.			
4.			
5.			
6.			
7.			
8.			
9.			
10.			
11.			
12.			
13.			
14.			
15.			
16.			
17.			

ANNOUNCEMENT/THANK-YOU LIST

NAME	ADDRESS	PRESENT	THANK-YOU NOTE SENT
18.			
19.			
20.			
21.			
22.			
23.			
24.			
25.			
26.			
27.			
28.			
29.			
30.			
31.			
32.			
33.			
34.			
35.			
36.			
37.			
38.			
39.			
40.			

CHOOSING A PEDIATRICIAN

A pediatrician is a doctor, certified by the American Academy of Pediatrics, who primarily treats children from birth through adolescence. If your baby will be delivered by your family doctor, you will probably continue with him or her as your child's doctor. If you will be delivered by an obstetrician, he or she will probably recommend a pediatrician or a pediatric clinic.

If you are new to the area, the American Medical Association suggests you contact your local Medical Society, listed in the telephone directory, for referrals. If you want to make an informed choice, you can consult library reference books (see Chapter One) to find out your prospective doctor's qualifications and affiliations. Try to interview a few doctors and make a final decision before your ninth month.

The general atmosphere of a doctor's office should be comfortably reassuring. The office support staff should be friendly and helpful. There should be a play area for waiting children and a distracting, cheerful decorating scheme to boost the morale of their worried parents.

During your interview, take note of the doctor's answer and manner. If the doctor seems bored with the same old questions, look for a doctor with a more enthusiastic approach. Does the doctor seem to genuinely like children? A bored pediatrician may not be up-to-date on training or looking for new ways to help your child. A good pediatrician should:

1. Take time to listen to you.

2. Consider your ideas and observations to be a valuable part of finding solutions to your child's problems.

3. Be part of a group practice or always easily accessible for consultation.

4. Be thorough and open, not giving you pat answers or prescribing drugs that merely mask discomfort.

If you do not have experience, some of your infant's behavior during the first weeks can be worrisome. Read some general baby-care books to get a working idea of what variations you can expect.

When should you call the pediatrician's office? Dr. Ramon Murphy, a pediatrician affiliated with Mt. Sinai Hospital, says, "You should call any time you are concerned about any aspect of your child's development, whether it is physical or psychological. The pediatrician's office should serve as a constant source of information for new parents and should answer any questions they have."

Dr. Murphy cautioned that some pediatricians might have more specific guidelines for when to call and you should discuss this during your prenatal interview. Although some new parents prefer a list of symptoms, a baby can be quite sick without any specific symptoms. You should feel free to consult your pediatrician when your intuition tells you that something is wrong. If your pediatrician makes you feel like a nuisance, change doctors.

Your baby's first pediatric visit will occur sometime between one and two months. During this visit the doctor will begin a personal and medical history and will test your baby for hereditary and metabolic disorders. Keep a notebook on your baby's day-to-day development so that on this and subsequent visits you can answer questions about eating and sleeping patterns, symptoms, and such milestones as sitting up for the first time.

At two months your baby will be given a DPT (diptheria-pertussis/whooping cough-tetanus) shot and a polio shot.

QUESTIONS FOR YOUR PEDIATRICIAN

- What training, practical experience, and hospital affiliation do you have?

- Is this a group practice? If not, can you always be reached? Is there another doctor available when you are not?

- What are your office hours?

- What is your policy on home visits?

- When will your first visit be?

- What is your fee and billing schedule? How are insurance forms dealt with in your office?

- What are your ideas about feeding and sleeping arrangements for infants?

- When is a good time to call your office?

- How often should my baby see you?

- Add your own questions below.

- _____

- _____

- _____

_____

_____

_____

_____

_____

_____

_____

_____

_____

_____

_____

_____

_____

_____

_____

_____

_____

_____

_____

_____

_____

_____

PEDIATRICIANS

DOCTOR'S NAME	ADDRESS/NUMBER	QUALIFICATIONS
1.		
2.		
3.		
4.		
5.		
6.		
7.		
8.		
9.		
10.		
11.		
12.		
13.		
14.		
15.		
16.		
17.		
18.		
19.		
20.		
21.		
22.		
23.		
24.		

A HELPING HAND

The average maternity stay has been reduced from seven or more days to about forty-eight hours. A Cesarean section requires a longer hospital stay and a longer convalescence. Some women resume a nearly normal schedule upon returning from the hospital, easily incorporating baby care into the routine. But these women are in the minority. It's hard to imagine how much chaos one tiny baby can inspire or how groggy and disoriented a few sleepless nights can make you. Most women need time to recover and rearrange their lives and some help with the daily chores is greatly appreciated. This time of adjustment can last anywhere from two weeks to two months. Try to enlist the services of your husband, your mother, your friends, a housekeeper, a housecleaning service, or a baby nurse.

If your husband is happy to help out, make sure he is going to be able to take the time off. If he works for a large company, have him discuss it with his Personnel Department. (It's not a good idea to plan your fixed vacation around your due date since the actual delivery date can be different.) Together you can plan a general schedule of housekeeping. Consider getting major chores (like window washing) out of the way in advance. Defrost your refrigerator and stock it full of frozen food.

Whether your mother or mother-in-law comes to help depends largely on your relationship with her. The help will not be worth much if it results in a battle of wills. Have a long discussion about newborn care and how you want to organize it, and deal with any conflicts in advance. If it seems like more trouble than comfort, explain tactfully that you have already arranged for some help and that she will not have to work hard but can just enjoy the baby instead.

Friends can contribute by providing meals, housecleaning, and babysitting. They can do the laundry for you, or the vacuum cleaning. True friends will understand that you might be too tired to entertain them.

Housekeeping help can be hired for a few weeks or even once a week to do the heavy jobs. There might be a teenager in your neighborhood willing to make some extra money this way.

Other time-savers include a diaper service, a laundromat, take-out food, letting your dishes drip dry, or using paper plates.

If you plan to hire a baby nurse, you should do so through a reputable agency that is licensed by your state and that follows the guidelines of the U.S. Department of Consumer Affairs. Your obstetrician, family doctor, pediatrician, nurse practitioner, or hospital can recommend one. These agencies schedule full-time permanent, full-time temporary, part-time permanent, and part-time temporary nursing, child care, and babysitting services.

You should call the child care agency six weeks before your due date. Some agencies will let you interview at least three nurses during that time. Others find it too difficult to schedule a particular nurse around such a variable date. It is preferable to interview so you do not have to deal with a stranger during your first weeks with baby. A nurse may be competent and qualified but not fit comfortably into your family.

A baby nurse's references are checked by the agency, and some agencies will let you double-check them yourself. The nurse needs to have completed the approved baby care course and have had practical experience in either midwifery or newborn nursery care.

What qualities do child care agencies look for in baby nurses? Carole Seskin of the Avalon Registry (a nursing and childcare agency) said that she looked for warmth, friendliness, a caring attitude, and "someone casual enough to get down on the floor and play with your baby." She especially liked child-care professionals who were enthusiastic about what they had chosen as their life's work and often brought in a photo album of the children they had helped to raise.

What questions should you ask a baby nurse during your interview? Ms. Seskin suggests that you discuss your ideas about babies and see if your caring styles are compatible. You should also ask about housework. Some nurses are happy to do it, but you should make up a job description of what you want done every day. You wouldn't appreciate accepting a job and on your first day having an extra four tasks assigned to you that you were never told about during your interview. Be specific.

Ms. Seskin also suggests that if you are having problems with your nurse you should talk them over frankly and directly with your nurse.

If you have decided to return to your job after a short leave of absence, try to finalize your permanent baby care arrangements now. See Chapter Twelve for your options.

Whatever form of help you choose, make sure you can depend on it and that all the details of how it will work are arranged in advance.

✓ CHECKLIST
THIS MONTH YOU SHOULD:

☐ Compile a shower guest list.

☐ Compile a shower present list—consult the Nursery and Layette Shopping Checklists (pages 62 and 71) for quantities.

☐ Compare and price different kinds of announcements.

☐ Compile an announcement mailing list.

☐ Buy a sheet of stamps now even if you plan to mail your announcements some time later.

☐ Get referrals and interview some pediatricians. Make a choice.

☐ Decide what kind of help you will enlist for the first week. If it's your husband or a relative, make definite plans. If it's a baby nurse, call an agency and start interviewing.

☐ Get any major cleaning chores out of the way. Defrost and stock up your refrigerator.

☐ Take a few childbirth preparation classes and practice your exercises at home. Keep up the good work. Practice makes perfect.

Add your own ideas below.

☐ _____

☐ _____

☐ _____

☐ _____

☐ _____

☐ _____

☐ _____

☐ _____

☐ _____

☐ _____

☐ _____

☐ _____

☐ _____

❧ NOTES AND OBSERVATIONS ❧

CHAPTER NINE

THE NINTH MONTH

PHYSICAL CHANGES

Lightening is a sensation that may be experienced by first-time mothers at any time during the last four weeks of pregnancy. The uterus, which has been expanding outward and upward for many months, suddenly shifts downward and forward in preparation for birth. You cannot only feel the difference but you can also see it in the altered shape of your stomach. Sometimes you can actually feel it happening since it can take only a few hours. Some women don't notice it happening but become suddenly aware that the sensation of pressure on their diaphragm has been replaced by pressure on their bladder. Second- or third-time mothers may not experience lightening until a week before, or even during, the beginning of labor.

The uterus now also increases the mild contractions you may have noticed throughout the pregnancy. They can become so frequent and intense that some women think they are starting labor. This is called false labor. Learn to recognize the signs and physical characteristics of real labor so that you can differentiate. If in doubt, rest and relax—these irregular contractions will then slow down or cease, unlike real labor contractions that intensify and become regular. Take a warm shower and drink a glass of wine. Real labor contractions will not be diminished or affected and a single glass of wine at this late date will, in my opinion, do no harm.

PSYCHOLOGICAL CHANGES

Emotional reactions during labor depend on your personality and your preparation but some are quite universal. Every woman, whether she lives in a mud hut or a skyscraper, wants to deliver in an environment she can trust, with a minimum of distraction and in the reassuring presence of someone she knows to have her best interests at heart.

It's generally easier for second-time mothers to give birth and it's not just for physical reasons. When you have had firsthand experience, you *know* that labor does not last forever. When you are in it for the first time, it's hard to believe it will end, no matter what you have read or heard.

Most women feel a sense of triumph and accomplishment when their baby is born. Intermingled with this is the puzzling perception that what once was one is now two. In the first weeks and especially in the first hours, you may feel as though you have been separated into two people or that you have been separated from a part of yourself. You feel an emotional hunger for your baby and feel less than whole when you two are not together. It does both mother and baby good to spend time together in the hours after birth and thus continue the relationship they've been having for nine months.

❧ SIGNS AND STAGES OF LABOR

SIGNS OF LABOR

There are three definitive signs of labor.

The first is called "the show" and happens when the blood-tinged plug of mucus that has sealed the cervix is discarded. Report this or any bleeding to your doctor.

The second sign is *the breaking of the bag of waters*. This can happen at any time within forty-eight hours of labor but usually happens during labor. Use a waterproof sheet under your bed in the last weeks, because there's a lot of amniotic fluid (the "waters"). Once the water breaks, don't use tampons or take a bath. Note the color of the fluid and report this to your doctor.

The third sign is *regular contractions that become stronger and occur closer together*. These may or may not be painful.

STAGES OF LABOR

First labors average twelve hours but may last twenty-four or more hours. Second and subsequent labors average from six to twelve hours. Labor rhythms vary and sometimes labor can stop and start over several days. The longest part of any labor is the first stage.

The First Stage is divided into three parts. The first part is called early labor. The cervix dilates (widens) and thins until the opening is about four centimeters across. Contractions are mild and short. If you're not planning to use anesthetics, you may eat lightly now (toast, jello, soup). Try to relax, take a warm shower, wash your hair, and master your relaxation/breathing techniques. Consult your doctor about when you should head for the hospital.

The second part is called active labor. The cervix dilates eight centimeters across and the contractions become longer and stronger. Massage and physical affection from your labor coach are helpful in counteracting any discomfort. Walking around and alternating different sitting and lying positions is also helpful, and some women enjoy the application of cold compresses.

The third part is called transition. This is when women may lose their tempers and their courage and most often request medication. It is also the shortest part of the first stage and the proverbial darkest hour before dawn. Your labor coach should remind you of how close you are when you reach this point.

The Second Stage happens when you are dilated to the necessary ten centimeters and is characterized by an overwhelming urge to push. This stage can last an hour with a first baby and can be as short as a few pushes with the second. The urge to push may frighten you but it is just what you need to do. Follow the doctor's instructions and use any breathing/relaxation techniques you have learned to avoid pushing unless it's absolutely necessary. Generally the vagina is naturally anesthetized at this stage by the pressure of baby's head.

When baby's head finally emerges, it's an inspiring moment for all who witness it. Baby's body is slimmer than the head and will follow easily, guided gently by helping hands.

CONGRATULATIONS! You did it!

The Third Stage will be anticlimatic while you're so busy celebrating and discovering your baby. It can take as much as an hour for the placenta to be expelled and for your uterus to start shrinking to its prepregnant proportions.

PACKING YOUR BAG(S)

Only about five percent of all women deliver on the projected date. Since you have a fifty percent chance of delivering up to two weeks earlier, you should pack what you will need in the hospital some time in advance.

If you decide to breastfeed you will now need to buy two or more nursing bras (see Chapter Four). Try these on—you have probably changed size already. You will also need two nursing nightgowns that either button down the front or have nursing slits that are otherwise invisible in the folds of the material. Simplicity Patterns has a good pattern for either style. The fabric you choose depends on the season, but since hopsitals tend to be well heated, you might choose a lighter fabric and take a robe or bed jacket.

If you have older children who will be spending the night at the home of a friend or a relative, pack an overnight bag for them and include a commemorative present or surprise.

What you will need in the hospital divides into three categories: labor and delivery aids, hospital stay articles, and babywear (the latter can be brought to the hospital by your visitors).

LABOR AND DELIVERY AIDS
(Childbirth instructors will have suggestions.)

☐ Socks

☐ Washcloths for compresses

☐ Cassette player and tapes

☐ Camera, video, and sound equipment for recording the event (These *must* be okayed by your doctor.)

☐ Fruit, crackers, seltzer, etc., for your labor coach

☐ Wine or champagne for celebrating afterwards

HOSPITAL STAY ARTICLES

☐ Two or more (nursing) nightgowns

☐ Two or more (nursing) bras

☐ One robe and/or bedjacket

☐ Slippers

☐ Cosmetics

☐ Perfume

☐ Brush and comb

☐ Toothbrush

☐ Toiletries (small quantities of toothpaste, soap, moisturizer, shampoo, and hair conditioner)

☐ Note paper, pens, your address book

☐ Reading material (this book?)

☐ Pictures of your family (older children will appreciate that you miss them).

NOTE: Do not pack prematernity clothes to wear coming home because you will not lose that much weight in such a short time.

BABYWEAR
☐ Diapers

☐ Clothes suitable to the weather

☐ Hat

☐ Receiving blankets/Bunting for cold weather

☐ Car seat (and padding)

Add your own suggestions below.

☐ _____

☐ _____

☐ _____

☐ _____

☐ _____

☐ _____

☐ _____

☐ _____

☐ _____

☐ _____

☐ _____

A TRIAL RUN

If you are having your baby anywhere other than at home, you have to think about how you are going to get to that place on your delivery day. Public transportation may be all right during your pregnancy but it's not reliable enough when time is of the essence. You may have driven for most of your pregnancy but you're too big to get behind the wheel now and labor can be too distracting. A taxi might work if you're close to the hospital but it's not as reassuring as a friend who knows you and knows the way.

Ideally you should have more than one person who is prepared to drive you to your hospital or birthing place. These drivers should have their cars checked and in good running order and keep their gasoline tanks full during the few weeks before the due date. They should be accessible by telephone and should make more than one trial run to your destination.

The trial run should take you both from your door to the parking place provided by the hospital. The trip should be made during rush hour, to judge maximum length, and in the middle of the day or at night, to judge the minimum length of the trip. Contrary to folklore and popular opinion, most babies are not born at night.

Explore alternative routes. If you live hours from the nearest hospital, you might start traveling when you begin labor and stop to rest and call your doctor from an intermediate place.

Use the pages provided to compose a list of vital telephone numbers and to map out routes. Include the number of your main driver, one or two alternate drivers, your husband, a place where you can leave a message for your husband if you can't reach him, your doctor, the local emergency service, and the local police station. If you have older children, include the number of a relative or babysitter who will come to your house to pick them up or stay with them.

<u>TRIAL RUN MAP AND ROUTES TO THE HOSPITAL/BIRTHING PLACE</u>

Time it took:

_____

_____

_____

_____

PHONE RELAY

NAME _____ TELEPHONE NUMBER(S)

_____

_____

_____

_____

_____

_____

_____

_____

_____

_____

_____

_____

_____

_____

_____

_____

_____

_____

_____

_____

_____

_____

EMERGENCY BIRTH

An emergency birth, at home or on the way to the hospital, is a very rare occurrence. Improved prenatal care and education and improved prenatal doctor-patient communication ensure that most women are aware of what labor involves and how their own labor is progressing.

If you live very far from the hospital or for some other reason are concerned about the possibility of an emergency birth, you might read and keep on hand one of the books listed below. Keep your list of emergency numbers in your hospital bag and keep a copy near every phone. Should you suddenly feel that you are further along in labor than you expected, don't panic. Call your doctor for advice. If you cannot get through to the doctor's office, call your local emergency service number or your local police station. One of these will get you medical help or an ambulance.

REFERENCES:

Emergency Childbirth
by Gregory J. White
Police Training Foundation
3412 Ruby Street
Franklin Park, IL 60131

Emergency Childbirth Handbook
by Barbara Anderson and Pamela Shapiro
Van Nostrand Reinhold

✓ CHECKLIST
THIS MONTH YOU SHOULD:

☐ Buy any necessary nursing items.

☐ Pack your hospital bag(s). Buy presents for any older children and prewash baby clothes being packed.

☐ Use a waterproof sheet under your regular sheets.

☐ Find two ways to arrive at your hospital or birthing place.

☐ Make at least two trial runs. Time them.

☐ Ask car drivers to make sure their cars are in optimum condition and their tanks full of gasoline.

☐ Keep your phone relay list handy. Keep emergency numbers near any phones.

☐ If you're concerned about the possibility, read up on emergency births.

☐ Learn the signs of labor.

☐ Get lots of rest and continue to practice your exercises.

Add your own ideas below.

☐ _____

☐ _____

☐ _____

☐ _____

☐ _____

❧ NOTES AND OBSERVATIONS ❧

CHAPTER TEN

BABY'S FIRST MONTH

PHYSICAL CHANGES

 Recovering from delivery is a slow process. Although you might even walk away from a nonmedicated delivery, your body will still need time to heal and to reorient itself to a nonpregnant state.

Whether you have a vaginal or Cesarean delivery, you will experience two or three weeks of a discharge called *lochia,* which is a result of your uterus shrinking. Lochia is at first a bright blood red that pales to pink and eventually becomes transparent. You should wear a sanitary pad, rather than tampon, as protection. You should not make love during this time and you should discuss with your obstetrician the issue of bathing versus showering.

Within three days your breasts will fill with milk. Some women find this painful, especially if they do not nurse and relieve the pressure. If you do not plan to breastfeed, wear a tight bra and relieve the pain with ice packs. At most the discomfort lasts only a few days.

If you have a vaginal delivery, you may have torn your vaginal area slightly, or you may have had an episiotomy—a small vaginal cut made surgically by your doctor during the delivery. Either of these, and the stretching of the vaginal muscles, can make you feel sore. Alternating applications of ice packs and heat can make your vaginal area feel better.

If you have an anesthetic you might feel groggy for the following twenty-four hours. If you have a Cesarean your recovery will be more complicated, because a Cesarean is a surgical procedure. It can be quite painful the first day and you may need help moving, sitting, and eating. If you want to breastfeed, you will need help from your husband or a nurse. The pain does heal quickly, though, and by the second day you will be getting up for short periods of time. You may suffer some painful indigestion due to the nature of the incision. Your general recovery will be slower but it will be complete. Having one Cesarean does not necessarily mean that your subsequent births will also have to be Cesareans.

PSYCHOLOGICAL CHANGES

Baby Blues (also known as postnatal depression) are not really all blues. Sometimes they're a rainbow of emotional states, of alternating flashes of elation and depression. Hormones are at least partially responsible. In the weeks after birth your body ceases production of all the hormones that made you feel content and tranquil during most of your pregnancy. To this chemical transformation add the tiring tasks of baby care, drastic changes in lifestyle, and some disturbed sleeping patterns, and you'll understand why some women end up in tears.

To these physical factors add some psychological ones, like the "great day syndrome." "It's a wonderful day," you might cry. "Why am I so depressed?" People are often unhappy or feel unstable after such great days as Christmas, their wedding, or the day their dreams came true. It's the natural kickback of having invested all your emotional energy in a future event. No matter how wonderful it is, it's hard for reality to live up to your expectations, and some people can't let go of the accumulated tension without crying or losing their temper.

It's also hard to realize beforehand just how much love a new baby can require or how vulnerable your love can make you feel. You may think that you surely cannot continue to give this much love forever. Or you might have enjoyed being the center of attention for nine months and now suddenly feel like baby's slave.

Some baby blues require therapy and counseling but most only require common sense. Remember to eat well, especially foods containing iron and vitamin B_6. Rest a lot and keep your life simple, and please don't expect too much of yourself. Every experience at mothering is a unique one and will develop its own rules. Use compassion in judging yourself. The chaos of the first weeks is very temporary. You will soon once again be in control of your time and your feelings.

YOUR BABY

. . . is equipped with an impressive assortment of survival mechanisms and is learning new skills every day. He learns to breathe in a minute after forty weeks of living in an airless environment, and can already search for and suck on a nipple but cannot yet differentiate hunger pangs from other pains. He can turn his head from side to side to avoid smothering but must still learn to regulate his own body temperature.

Your newborn is quite sensitive to light and will blink or shut his eyes at a bright one. The baby can't focus sharply on anything more than about eight inches away. He cannot distinguish colors yet but he can see varying degrees of brightness, and three dimensions. He seems most curious about faces and facelike objects.

Baby prefers the sound of a soft, high-pitched voice. A loud noise will startle him and make him cry.

Baby's heart beats about 120 times a minute and he breathes 33 times a minute, both of which are twice the rate of an adult. His head is about a quarter of his body length, whereas an adult's is about an eighth of the body length. His arms and legs also seem small in relation to his torso and he holds them close to him. His tiny hands are clenched and ready to grab onto something.

All newborn babies love to be held and cuddled and their soft skin and sweet smell seems to invite affection.

⚜ FIRST WEEKS

Regard these first weeks as a honeymoon, a chance to learn all about your baby as he or she learns about the world. This time can be hypnotically interesting and quite bewildering. It's best to concentrate on just your baby. In fact, it's hard to concentrate on anything else.

Nourishment, comfort, and protection were supplied continuously before the baby was born. Now they have become intermittent and, to the baby, confusingly changeable. In this strange new world your baby needs the reassurance that his or her needs will continue to be met as they were before birth.

Can you spoil a newborn? No, not yet. The thinking of newborns is not developed enough for them to imagine that they are capable of controlling your actions. All they can think about is what they feel at the moment. They are not even sure where you end and they begin.

Your baby is not as finished as you might think. A baby is not a miniature adult with corresponding, smoothly running systems. A newborn's nervous and digestive systems still need to mature, and although they can recognize light and dark, they have no idea that nighttime is for sleeping through.

Every newborn will have a personal pattern of sleeping and feeding. Most babies sleep seventy-five percent of the time but some newborns will be awake at least half of the day. A newborn might want to be fed eight times a day. Another might want to be fed twelve times in twenty-four hours (which means you won't get any regular sleep for a few weeks).

All babies tend to regularize their schedules and lengthen their night sleeping time some time between ten days and three weeks after birth. It takes that long for a newborn to adjust, whether you set the schedule or the baby sets it. Putting your baby on a fixed feeding schedule at birth is a good way to make yourself miserable. Your baby has no sense of time and may cry the whole time he or she is waiting to be fed, making both of you more tense. Baby is not trying to indoctrinate you with nighttime waking but you may feel somewhat brainwashed after a few weeks. This is a very temporary arrangement and so soon ended that one day you might look back at this time with nostalgia. The best thing to do is relax and enjoy this time with your baby and eliminate all the distractions you can.

Here are some tips for making the most of your first weeks with your baby:
• Prepare everything in advance. Know how to fold a diaper and sterilize a bottle. Clean and stock your house with lots of food and supplies. Have your baby's things ready. Have a helping hand.
• Keep a practical baby book in the house. Dr. Spock or Dr. Leach (see the Reading appendix) can be very reassuring when you're worried about the baby's spitting up or your own burping procedure.
• Don't listen to well-meaning advice about scheduling or about how you might be spoiling your baby. Tests have proven that babies fed on demand grow into secure, not spoiled, children. Cuddle and feed your baby when he or she needs it and tell anyone who disagrees that you're following your doctor's advice.
• Unless this disturbs your sleep further, keep the baby near you in the first weeks. It makes baby care easier and the baby can always be moved into the nursery once the schedule is predictable.
• Try to sleep whenever you can. If you run around with the vacuum cleaner whenever baby nods off, you'll be crazy in a matter of weeks.
• Avoid cooking. Have someone else do it or serve catered, take-out, thawed and heated, or ready-to-eat food on your good china and by candlelight.
• Ask visitors to keep it brief. Say that your doctor advised fifteen-minute visits. If they want to visit longer, they can cook up a meal, serve it to you, eat

with you, wash the dishes, and leave after dessert. If your Aunt Tilly wants to come all the way from Kalamazoo and fifteen minutes is impractical, ask her to come next month.

• Keep the baby warm and cozy. Seventy-five degrees is the minimum temperature for an unclothed baby. Some babies like being snugly wrapped in blankets no matter what the temperature. Most babies prefer to wear socks or otherwise have their feet covered.

• Although you don't have to go around whispering, it's best to keep the baby's room quiet and darkened in the beginning. Some continuous background noise like fans, the hum of a vacuum cleaner, or a radio softly playing is even soothing.

• Babies are given only sponge baths until the umbilical cord heals. Remember to keep the room and the water warm and to have your bath supplies handy. Wet babies are slippery, and while there are a variety of bathing techniques, you will always need to use both hands. A baby can be bathed in a bath or a dishtub. If a baby dislikes being bathed, you can keep it to a minimum, sponge-bathing the baby's diaper area and head only when necessary.

• Unplug the world for these weeks. Let the mail pile up. Don't answer the phone. You can catch up with the news next month but your baby will never be this tiny again. It's easier for everyone if you align yourself with the baby's rhythm and if your family makes some time and space for its newest member.

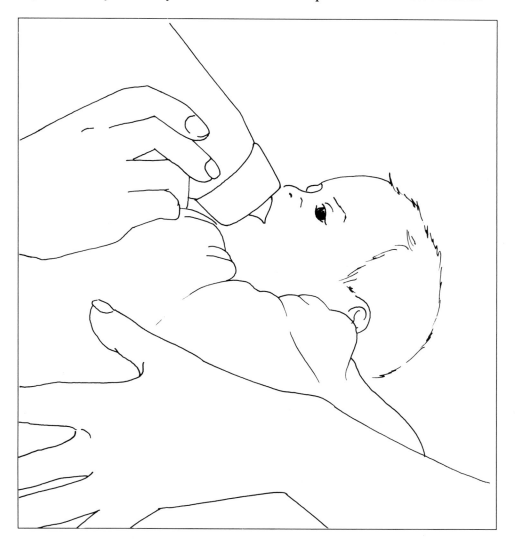

BABY'S FIRST PHOTOGRAPHS

Paste down as many as you can fit on the page!

BABY'S FIRST PHOTOGRAPHS

Paste down as many as you can fit on the page!

FIRST HOURS AND DAYS

Even though your new baby is indisputably the most beautiful baby ever born, he or she may not look exactly as you expected. Some of the following typical newborn characteristics can cause a parent to be unnecessarily concerned.

The adjustment to the cooler temperature of the delivery room may leave your baby's soon-to-be rosy skin temporarily mottled or the hands and feet temporarily bluish or purple. Light-skinned babies may have dull pink patches or "strawberry" birthmarks on their necks and eyelids that you might mistake for a rash. Dark-skinned babies may have slate-blue patches on their lower back or buttocks. Both kinds of discolorations will fade and disappear during the first years. All babies are born covered with a cheesy, white substance, called the vernix caseosa, that protected them in the amniotic sac. This is washed off in the first bath or may be absorbed into their skin as a moisturizer.

Babies may also have bruises or marks from the delivery that take a few days to fade. Baby's head can be temporarily misshapen or molded by its passage through the birth canal. The bony plates of the skull reshape during the process to decrease the size of the head without damaging the brain. In a few days the skull resumes its normal shape.

Babies may have blistered lips or calloused thumbs from in-utero thumb sucking. Their eyes may be crossed but this, too, will correct itself.

None of these blemishes affect your baby in any permanent way. Besides, they are minor compared to the wonder you feel at the emergence of a tiny human being that you have helped create.

A baby's first physical examination begins before birth is complete. As the head emerges and turns, the doctor examines the nose and mouth to make sure the baby can breathe freely.

One minute after birth and again at five minutes after birth, the baby is given the Apgar Test. Originated by and named after Dr. Virginia Apgar, an anesthesiologist, this test measures a baby's heart rate and pulse, breathing and muscle tone, response to stimulus, and appearance and color, rating them on a scale of one to ten. Seven is considered a normal score. This test does not indicate anything about the baby's future health or potential. It only helps the doctor to know if the baby needs any immediate special care.

After the umbilical cord is clamped and cut, the baby is patted dry, kept warm, and is examined thoroughly, every toe and finger counted. Your child will be measured and weighed, identifying handprint and/or footprint taken, and a plastic I.D. bracelet that matches yours will be put on the baby's wrist. The baby may be given an injection of vitamin K to reduce bleeding and may have a blood sample taken. Drops of silver-nitrate solution or an antibiotic ointment are placed in the eyes to prevent infection, although this can be delayed until after baby and his family have had some time together.

Doctors will also determine your baby's true age by the development of certain physical characteristics. Babies born before thirty-seven weeks or weighing under five pounds are considered premature and may be kept in a hospital incubator until they reach a normal birth weight.

How much you see of your baby during the first days depends on the hospital's (or alternative birthing place's) policies, whether you have rooming in, and your child's health. During the first days in a hospital, the baby will receive physical and neurological examinations and a PKU test. The PKU test screens for a metabolic disorder that can be treated by diet. This test is often repeated at your first pediatric visit.

BIRTH RECORD

Date of Arrival _____

Time of Arrival _____

Place of Arrival _____

_____

Delivered by _____

Birth attended by _____

_____

Baby's First Name _____

Baby's Middle Name(s) _____

Baby's Last Name _____

Baby was named after _____

Birth Weight _____

Birth Length _____

Color of Hair _____

Color of Eyes _____

Birthmarks _____

Family Resemblances _____

_____

First Impressions _____

_____

_____

_____

_____

_____

_____

_____

_____

_____

_____

_____

_____

_____

_____

_____

_____

_____

_____

_____

_____

_____

HANDPRINT AND FOOTPRINT

Just before bath time, touch your baby's hand and foot to a stamp pad that has water-soluble, nontoxic ink. Then press them down on this page. Wash the ink off with a soapy washcloth. You can also place the hand and foot on this page and trace an outline around them.

BABY MEMORABILIA

Use this page to save any pictures, keepsakes, and information about your baby's first months. The baby will grow so quickly you'll be happy to have these remembrances of this wonderful time.

✓ **CHECKLIST**
THIS MONTH YOU SHOULD:

☐ Eat well, rest a lot, unplug your phone, and enjoy your baby.

☐ Keep notes of what the baby does. If you're too preoccupied to use the pages for notes and observations, paste in more pictures of the baby or of baby cards you receive.

Add your own ideas below.

☐ _____

☐ _____

☐ _____

☐ _____

☐ _____

☐ _____

☐ _____

☐ _____

☐ _____

☐ _____

☐ _____

☐ _____

❄ NOTES AND OBSERVATIONS ❄

CHAPTER ELEVEN

BABY'S SECOND MONTH

PHYSICAL CHANGES

Your postpartum checkup is usually given at six weeks after your delivery. During this checkup your doctor will examine your uterus to make sure it has resumed its normal shape. He or she may test you for anemia. Breastfeeding mothers should continue to take their vitamins and iron supplements. Your weight will be monitored, your blood pressure taken, and your breasts will be examined.

This is a good time to talk about further birth control and family planning. Your first period can arrive at any time from six to twenty-four weeks after delivery but you can ovulate before then. Breastfeeding does reduce ovulation but does not prevent it. It's not wise to breastfeed while you are pregnant with a second child, and you cannot take birth control pills if you are breastfeeding. A diaphragm that fit you before you became pregnant might not fit anymore and should be checked by your gynecologist/obstetrician. If you have any questions about making love after delivery, ask your doctor. It is not always easy the first time after having a baby but this too passes.

This is a good time to begin exercising again, even if you have had a Cesarean delivery. Your figure will have regained some of its normal proportions by now but exercise can speed up what's left of the normalizing process and give you extra energy.

You can join an exercise class that you can take the baby to, or you can work out at home, including baby in your program or letting him watch from his infant seat. If the weather's nice you can take long walks or jog behind your stroller.

PSYCHOLOGICAL CHANGES

A baby can give new dimension to a couple's love for each other or can create serious tension. Working out problems in your relationship before the baby arrives helps but sometimes a baby can create problems you've never dreamed of, because:

• There's no longer the time or the opportunity for the two of you to work out problems the way you did before.

• No matter how well two people related to each other romantically, there is no way to tell how they will relate to each other as parents until they are parents.

• A husband can feel jealous of the attention a baby gets, especially if he is reliving the birth of a brother or sister. Children express feelings of jealousy dramatically. A husband might be so embarrassed by his jealous feelings for a tiny, helpless creature that he won't even admit it to himself.

• A wife can feel overwhelmed by her hormonal adjustments, her increased housework, and the shifting of roles that happens when a couple has a baby.

These problems can be worked out and this period of transition and adjustment can make a marriage stronger and more intense, but frank communication and a willingness to change and grow are required. Here are some tips for making this adjustment:

• You have to work, even in this busy time, to create time together, whether it's shared work or time alone. Even a walk will do. You should discuss your feelings with each other no matter how trivial they might seem.

• If you disagree with your mate's approach to parenting, it's important to talk things out. Discuss it until you arrive at a compromise on parenting styles. One method of child rearing is not necessarily right or wrong. Avoid using the words right and wrong. Express yourself tactfully and remember that each parenting style has good points and bad points. Different styles might work in different situations or with a different child. If you still don't like the parent your mate is, have patience. This is a period of gradual transition.

• Continue to be affectionate and considerate of each other. Parenthood is happening to both of you, and while women often bear the hormonal brunt of childbearing, men can also feel vulnerable and open to rejection. Take the time to laugh together and to plan an inspiring future based on your dreams of a happy family.

• Share baby care, even if the mother is the one who stops working (temporarily) to stay home. This helps the husband know what's involved and gives the wife a chance to be objective about her life.

 # YOUR BABY

. . . is becoming a creature of habit. Except for a few days every now and then, she will have a regular pattern of eating and sleeping and will most likely sleep five to seven hours between feedings during the night. You will notice preferences and a personal style of eating or sleeping. A breastfed baby might prefer one breast to the other. Some babies will prefer one sleeping position to another.

Her eyes can now track a moving object and can focus on objects that are twelve inches away. Your child will enjoy watching you from the infant chair, making noises in response to sounds, and enjoy bath time splashing and looking in mirrors.

It will make you happy to realize how happy she is to see you. When you walk into view, she might wave arms and legs and make excited noises. Sometime this month your baby may give you her first smile.

Her general movements are becoming more graceful and controlled. She can hold objects for a minute and, by the end of the month, will be able to lift her head. Don't worry about the baby's sneezes and hiccups, because neither is cause for concern. The baby will weight about twelve pounds and will be about twenty-three inches long.

⚜ CRYING AND COLIC

The crying of a small baby can be quite disturbing. Nature arranged it that way so a newborn's needs would be responded to immediately. No amount of forewarning will prepare you for the way the baby's cries will wrench your heart.

Crying is a baby's major language at first. It will all start out sounding equally urgent·but with a few weeks experience you will be able to distinguish between cries of hunger and pain and just plain grumbling.

Some babies are troubled by colic in the first few months. Colic is the name given to long, frantic bouts of crying. It may begin at any time during the first three months but usually starts at six weeks. Colic can last a few weeks or, in rare cases, many months. A baby will start to cry at a specific time, before or after a feeding and usually in the evening between six and ten, and nothing will seem to comfort the baby for very long.

Everything has been blamed for colic. Perhaps there are a variety of interacting causes, but the most likely one is the immaturity of the nervous and digestive systems. If you have to comfort a colicky baby, here are some tips that might make both you and baby happier:

- If you are using formula, try another formula since the baby might be allergic to the first one.

- If you are breastfeeding, your baby might be allergic to foods you're eating or drugs you're taking, or might be overstimulated by your excess caffeine intake.

- Sometimes a few drops of fennel tea with sugar, given by spoon before feeding, will help quiet down the baby's stomach. This solution is bottled and sold in England as "gripe water."

- A hot-water bottle one-third filled with *warm* water, tightly sealed, and wrapped in a towel and placed under the baby's stomach can help. You can also hold the baby with the stomach pressing on your shoulder bone or with your hand firmly but gently pressing on the stomach.

- If you have no objection to pacifiers, try one. Nurses use a bottle nipple stuffed with cotton and sealed with cardboard, which they attach to a folded diaper so the baby can always find it.

- A rocking chair might be a way to soothe baby and let you rest at the same time.

- A Snugli carrier is a way to comfort the baby with your movements and body warmth while you get some work done.

- Ear plugs dim the sounds of crying. You can still hear the baby but it's not as loud.

- Don't feel like a villain if you need to escape and there is not another set of arms waiting to relieve you. If the baby is fed, changed, checked for causes of pain, and still continues to cry, it is all right to place him or her in bed for a few minutes while you grab a shower or a cup of coffee. A few minutes of crying won't harm the baby and may make you feel more able to cope.

- If that's not enough, hire a sitter and go out for a few hours.

- Don't take colic personally. It just happens to some babies and it is not a reflection of either your ability to mother or your child's future development.

• An excellent book on colic and comforting is:

Crying Baby, Sleepless Nights
by Sandy Jones
Warner Books

BABY'S BIRTH ANNOUNCEMENT

Paste baby's birth announcement here and frame one for the nursery.

BIRTH ANNOUNCEMENT FROM THE NEWSPAPER

If you placed an announcement in a local paper or in an association publication, clip it out and paste it here.

FAMILY HISTORY

Becoming parents can generate interest in your own direct ancestors. Create and keep a record of your immediate family history. Ask older relatives to help gather information. Send away for certificates. Try to gather baby pictures as far back as you can. Your baby will appreciate this wealth of information when he or she is older.

Baby's Name _____ Time/Place of Birth _____

Mother's Name _____ Time/Place of Birth _____

Father's Name _____ Time/Place of Birth _____

Maternal Grandmother _____ Time/Place of Birth _____

Maternal Grandfather _____ Time/Place of Birth _____

Paternal Grandmother _____ Time/Place of Birth _____

Paternal Grandfather _____ Time/Place of Birth _____

Maternal
Great-Grandmother #1 _____ Time/Place of Birth _____

Maternal
Great-Grandfather #1 _____ Time/Place of Birth _____

Maternal
Great-Grandmother #2 _____ Time/Place of Birth _____

Maternal
Great-Grandfather #2 _____ Time/Place of Birth _____

Paternal
Great-Grandmother #1 _____ Time/Place of Birth _____

Paternal
Great-Grandfather #1 _____ Time/Place of Birth _____

Paternal
Great-Grandmother #2 _____ Time/Place of Birth _____

Paternal
Great-Grandfather #2 _____ Time/Place of Birth _____

LOCK OF BABY'S HAIR

BABY'S I.D. BRACELET

Put your own here, too, if you like.

BABY PHOTOGRAPHS

Be sure to get at least one snapshot of the baby with the father, siblings, grandparents. Take a picture of the baby at bath time, sleeping in the crib, and playing with first toys.

✓ **CHECKLIST**

THIS MONTH YOU SHOULD:

☐ Save and paste in the baby's I.D. bracelet, a lock of hair, and any photographs you take.

☐ Start gathering information for a family history. There's no rush, since this is usually a slow process.

☐ Mail the birth announcements.

☐ Take the baby for at least one checkup and the first immunization.

☐ Have your first postpartum checkup and discuss birth control with your doctor.

☐ Start an exercise program. If you're breastfeeding, continue to pay extra attention to your diet.

☐ Take time to be together as a couple. Talk to your husband and share your feelings.

Add your own ideas below.

☐ _____

☐ _____

☐ _____

☐ _____

☐ _____

☐ _____

☐ _____

☐ _____

☐ _____

☐ _____

☐ _____

☐ _____

☐ _____

☐ _____

☐ _____

❧ NOTES AND OBSERVATIONS ❧

CHAPTER TWELVE

BABY'S THIRD MONTH

PHYSICAL CHANGES

Having some of your former energy back means remembering and wanting to resume some of your former interests and activities. This might mean an occasional night out for you and your husband or it might mean resuming your career. It's time to think about some form of child care. If you're on leave from your job, you no doubt have a definite plan of action.

PSYCHOLOGICAL CHANGES

More than half of all mothers in America today work outside of the home. Should you work? Only your needs and goals can answer that question.

In former generations it was assumed that a woman would quit work to have a family. Now it is assumed that women will train for a career and only interrupt it briefly for childbearing. Your own decision should be influenced by what you need and enjoy and not by anyone else's assumptions or expectations.

Make a list of your goals and needs and try to figure out the best way to fulfill them while still spending the maximum of valuable time with your growing child. Be honest with yourself. There's lots of improvisation (and compromise) possible.

You might work part time or freelance. You might be able to start your own business or work out of your own home. Perhaps your goals can be delayed or worked on in small ways until your children are older, or perhaps the time to act is now so that your children can benefit from your decision later.

When should you return to work? Again, only you can know. Staying home during the baby's first three months gives you a chance to get well acquainted and makes the baby easier to care for. Staying home for the baby's first three years is a wonderful opportunity although not always possible or desirable. Some mothers enjoy staying home until their children go off to college and others get restless when their two-year-old gets more independent.

The important thing is to be happy with the decision you make. Your child will note and inherit your sense of accomplishment and contentment whether you are the Chairman of the Board or the Chairman of the PTA. Unfortunately, this also holds true for feelings of unhappiness and resentment.

Planning, intuition, and good sense have brought you safely and happily through your first year of mothering (nine months of pregnancy and three months of tending). Be proud of yourself and what you've accomplished. Mothering is a valuable experience and a skill that can be applied to many other areas of expertise.

YOUR BABY

. . . is becoming more sociable and is a real pleasure to be with. He not only recognizes his mother with a smile but he can recognize different members of the family. Your baby likes company and takes part in conversations, listening carefully, waiting for a pause in the conversation, and then offering baby-talk observations that imitate your speech patterns. Baby can bubble and gurgle and coo.

Cuddling is no longer enough. With an attention span of forty-five minutes, your baby is eager to learn all about colors, shapes, and textures, and can see everything in the room. His hands, no longer clenched tightly at his side, can find and grasp objects, and bring them to his mouth for baby's truest method of testing new discoveries.

The rough time of colic and repeated middle-of-the-night feedings is over for most babies. If baby still wakes and fusses occasionally during the night, it might be a good idea to wait and see if he will fall asleep again spontaneously. By now, baby has developed a memory for patterns and for cause and effect.

By three months of age, baby can lift head and chest when lying on his stomach, and will weigh between thirteen and fifteen pounds and be about twenty-four inches long.

✤GOING OUT AND GOING BACK TO WORK

Consider the following alternatives to child care and choose the one most suitable to your living and working styles.

- **Babysitting** is useful for an occasional night out or even for a regular afternoon session. A relative or neighbor might consider doing you the favor or you could hire a local teenager or even a professional from a child-care agency.

If the sitter has child-care experience, you only have to explain and note the basics of your baby's schedule and behavior. For the inexperienced sitter, you should leave specific, *written* instructions and a practical child-care book (see Reading appendix). You should actually run through the baby's basic routines of feeding and diapering together—remember how intimidating it originally seemed to you. Also be sure to leave several phone numbers (and names) for the sitter—where you can be reached, the baby's pediatrician, a neighbor, another relative, and some emergency numbers.

- **Live-in help** is ideal in terms of flexibility and a bonus if you work long, irregular hours. Nowadays it is hard to find and it is the most expensive child-care arrangement. You also need the space to accommodate live-in help and will have to make some adjustments for sharing your space. Hired, live-in help is screened and referred through a child-care agency.

You might also find a college student who would enjoy doing day care in exchange for room and board, or an older relative who might want to move in and help you out.

- **Daily help at home** can also be a relative. No one has a more vested interest in your infant than a grandmother or a doting aunt, although these days grandmothers and aunts may have jobs of their own. This is also not a practical solution if you and the person involved disagree on child care.

A hired daily helper is also screened by a child-care agency, but you should interview that person just as you would a temporary baby nurse (see Chapter Eight). This is also a comparatively expensive option although if you can find someone who is willing to do housework as well, it might not cost you much more than the cost of having a housecleaning service. It certainly is nice to come home from work to a clean house and a fed baby.

- **Family-centered child care** means taking your child to someone else's home, usually a woman with children of her own. She should not be caring for more than four children under twelve, including her own. You can find suitable candidates through friends or religious and social organizations, such as the YMCA, the Red Cross, or the Jewish Community Council. You should interview these caretakers in their own homes. Whether or not you feel comfortable is an important clue as to whether or not your child will.

Are her children friendly and happy? Does she seem to genuinely like children? Is her home reasonably clean, safe, and equipped with baby paraphernalia? Is her home convenient to where you work and live? Will transportation be a problem?

Be sure to ask for her rules about bringing a sick baby to her, since that is a time where in-home help has a definite advantage. Will she notify you when her children are sick? Despite this disadvantage, family-centered care is still a good bet. It is flexible, relatively inexpensive, and often an enjoyable, stimulating experience for your child.

• **Shared care** is a version of in-home care (in one home or a rotation of homes) where the cost of child care is shared by more than one parent.

• **A Parent's Co-op** is shared care on a larger scale in which a group of neighbors or friends jointly hire and supervise childcare personnel.

• **A day-care center** is regulated by the state (except in Florida and Mississippi) and is often the easiest child care to find although the center may have a long waiting list. A center is required by law to have one staff member for every ten children.

To evaluate a day-care center you should interview them by telephone and then spend at least one morning at each center. Note safety standards, equipment, staff, and how the staff interacts with the children. Note their program of activities. Is it creative and stimulating? Day-care centers are not flexible about hours and will charge extra for overtime.

A baby who is less than a year old will really benefit from individual attention and might be better off in a one-to-one or family-centered child care situation. Children less than two years old rarely play together so having other children around, unless they are older and help care for the baby, is not really an advantage. You might start out with more individualized care and put your name on a waiting list for a day-care center.

Use your intuition to judge which method will suit your baby and your work needs. Always interview first by phone. If you're interested, follow up with a personal interview of at least one hour. Ask straightforward, open-ended questions. Check references. Remember that a certain amount of your child-care costs are tax deductible and in some cases may be subsidized by government or community agency.

BABYPROOFING THE HOUSE

Within a few months your baby will be mobile enough to start exploring the darkest corners of your house. Is your house safe enough for baby exploration? You might say yes, but are you thinking of adult safety standards?

Try seeing things from a baby's point of view. Go through every room in the house and carefully look at everything. Take note of which objects are at baby level, which objects are breakable, which are small enough for a baby's mouth (coins, buttons, safety pins, paper clips, etc.). Note any sharp corners on furniture or any heavy objects that a baby could pull down. What everyday objects and substances would be poisonous if swallowed by a baby or toddler?

If two people attack this problem, you'll have the benefit of two pairs of eyes and two approaches to solving safety problems. First list any hazards that might occur in more than one room. Then run through your house one room at a time looking for specific problems. Some hazards will have to be permanently eliminated, others temporarily locked away or simply placed out of reach until the baby is older.

You can't remove everything a baby could break or be hurt by. The baby will have to learn the meaning of the word "no" at some point but it's simpler to rearrange your furniture than it is to constantly be chasing after a toddler.

Use the Baby Safety Checklist for a guideline.

BABY SAFETY CHECKLIST

NOTES

General Safety Rules:

☐ Windows that baby can reach should have safety bars or safety locks.

☐ Safety locks should be used on all cabinets containing chemicals such as: ammonia, antifreeze, bleach, boric acid, detergents, furniture polish, hair dyes, insecticides, lighter fluid, nail polish, perfume, shaving lotion, silver polish, super glue, turpentine. *(For a complete list contact your local poison control center.)*

☐ Place out of reach any sharp or breakable objects (glasses, knives, etc.).

☐ Use stair guards.

☐ Do not use kerosene heaters. Never leave a baby near a fire or an electric heater. Enclose and block radiators. Put matches and lighters in a safe place.

☐ Fill empty electrical sockets with plugs. Replace frayed wires and fasten excess wiring to discourage the baby from pulling on them.

☐ Common household and garden plants can be poisonous to varying degrees. Even some edible garden plants can have seeds, leaves, or vines that are dangerous. Learn the names of your plants. Some poisonous ones are: avocado leaves, azaleas, daffodils, dieffenbachia, hyacinths, ivies (many varieties), mistletoe, oleander, periwinkle, philodendrons, rhododendron *(For a complete list of poisonous house and garden plants, contact your local poison control center.)*

☐ Never leave plastic bags of any variety or size anywhere a young child find them. Do not use these for mattress covers.

☐ Never leave cigarettes lying around. A single cigarette can make a one-year-old quite sick.

Baby Room Guidelines:

☐ Use government and industry standards (see Chapter Six) when buying baby furniture, toys, and toyboxes.

☐ Do not place a crib near a window.

☐ Do not leave baby powders, ointments, or safety pins within the baby's reach.

☐ Remove playthings that the baby can use to climb out of the crib.

Bathroom Guidelines:

☐Lock up cleaning and cosmetic supplies or anything stored in a glass bottle.

☐Keep hairdriers and electrical equipment away from the bath and sink. *Unplug them when not in use because they can cause harm even when they are switched off.*

☐Place rubber mats or nonskid decals on the bathtub floor.

☐Babies love to throw things into the toilet so you might consider locking the bathroom when it is not in use. *Locks on the inside of the door should be removed.*

Kitchen Guidelines:

☐As soon as possible, teach the baby that stoves and microwaves are dangerous. You can let the baby feel their heat from a distance as you say "Hot!" and "Ow!" several times, dramatically.

☐Keep pan handles turned away from the outer edge of the stove. Boil water on the back burner.

☐Lock away cleaning supplies or anything stored in glass. Leave the baby one cabinet with pans and plastic cooking equipment to rummage in safely.

☐Save tablecloths for special occasions, because babies love to yank at them.

BABY SAFETY INFORMATION
For safety information and tips, contact:

Your local poison control center
consult your telephone directory.

American Academy of Pediatrics
141 Northwest Post Road
Elk Grove Village, Illinois 60007
(800) 424-9393

U.S. Consumer Product Safety Commission
Consumer Hotline – (800) 638-2772

Two useful books on safety and first aid are:

Childproofing Your Home
by Arlene Stewart
Addison Wesley

A Sigh Of Relief
by Martin Green
Bantam Books

BABY PLAY

Playing with a baby increases the child's curiosity, creativity, and intelligence. Playing involves more than toys. A simple game like peek-a-boo can teach the baby about cause and effect, while your daily activities made into games can teach a baby to be interested and involved in the world.

Talking to your baby is important. As you go through your daily routine together, be sure to tell the baby what you are doing and to name the people, places, and things you see. Babies love rhythmic speech, such as nursery rhymes and singing. They enjoy dancing in their mother's arms. You can teach a baby to make music with a rattle or by clapping hands.

Baby exercise and massage can help a baby be aware of and enjoy his or her body. There are several informative books on both subjects but if you remember to be gentle you can probably improvise, using what you enjoy as a source of inspiration. Perhaps baby exercise can be incorporated into your own exercise program.

As soon as your baby is comfortable in the infant seat or playpen, bring him or her into the center of family activity and let baby watch you when you work. Talk at first about what you're doing and later on give the baby something relevant to hold, like a cooking spoon. Babies love to be a part of what's going on, especially if you make it seem like fun.

By three months babies appreciate and benefit from the stimulation of excursions. They will enjoy coming along for visits, walks, shopping, exercise classes, and, in some cases, work. Having a baby is a unique opportunity to introduce a curious newcomer to the wonders of your world.

BABY PHOTOGRAPHS

BABY PHOTOGRAPHS

BABY PHOTOGRAPHS

✓**CHECKLIST**
THIS MONTH YOU SHOULD:

☐ Investigate baby exercise and massage and incorporate these into your now *regular* postpartum exercise sessions.

☐ Make a list and a plan of action for babyproofing your house. The next months will go by faster than you think.

☐ Consider going out, resuming hobbies, or going back to work.

☐ Investigate child care. Set up interviews when necessary.

☐ Congratulate yourself on a year of mothering! Good luck!

Add your own ideas below.

☐ _____
☐ _____
☐ _____
☐ _____
☐ _____
☐ _____
☐ _____
☐ _____
☐ _____
☐ _____
☐ _____
☐ _____
☐ _____
☐ _____
☐ _____
☐ _____
☐ _____
☐ _____
☐ _____
☐ _____
☐ _____
☐ _____
☐ _____
☐ _____
☐ _____
☐ _____
☐ _____

❧ Notes and observations ❧

THE FIRST MONTH

American College of Obstetricians and Gynecologists
600 Maryland Avenue SW
Washington, DC 20024
(202) 638-5577

American College of Nurse-Midwifery
15 K Street NW
Suite 1120
Washington, DC 20005
(202) 347-5445

American Society for Psychoprophylaxis in Obstetrics
(ASPO)
1840 Wilson Boulevard
Suite 204
Arlington, VA 22201
(703) 524-7802

National Association of Childbearing Centers
RD No. 1
Perkiominville, PA 18074
(215) 234-8068

BEAUTY AND FASHION

For maternity catalogues and store addresses:

Lady Madonna
561 Richmond Street West
Toronto, Ontario, Canada M5V 146
1-800-387-2026

Mothers Work
P.O. Box 40121
Philadelphia, PA 19106

ReCreations Maternity
Wardrobe Catalog
P.O. Box 091038
Columbus, OH 43209

BIRTH PREPARATION

Conscious Childbearing
(formerly called the Cesarean Birth Alliance)
(516) 596-0959
(516) 781-0785
(9 AM to 9 PM)

International Childbirth Education Association
80–60 26th Avenue South
Bloomington, MN 55420
(612) 854-8660

PRODUCT SAFETY GUIDELINES

American Academy of Pediatrics
Division of Health Education
141 Northwest Post Road
Elk Grove Village, IL 60007
(800) 424-9393
(for car seat information)

Juvenile Products Manufacturers Association
66 East Main Street
Moorestown, NJ 08057
(609) 234-9155

U.S. Consumer Product Safety Commission
Consumer Hotline (800) 638-CPSC or (800) 638-2772

U.S. Department of Transportation
National Highway Safety Administration
400 Seventh Street SW
Washington, DC 20590
(202) 426-1828
(for car seat information)

PRODUCT SOURCES

The Mothers Today Source Book
Mothers Today Magazine
441 Lexington Avenue
New York, NY 10017
($3.50 per copy)

PLAYTIME SAFETY INFORMATION

Send a postcard with name, address, and zip code. Only one address per postcard
and one request per family to:

"A.B.C. Toy Booklet"
Toy Manufacturers of America, Inc.
P.O. Box 866
Madison Square Station
New York, NY 10159
(one booklet is free)

or call:
U.S. Consumer Product Safety Commission
Consumer Hotline (800) 638-CPSC or (800) 638-2772

WORKING MOTHERS

Send a self-addressed, stamped envelope to:

Mothers' Home Business Network
P.O. Box 423
East Meadow, NY 11554
(support system for mothers who work at home)

DOCTORING BABY

"Ten Guides to Proper Medicine Use"
The Council on Family Health
420 Lexington Avenue
New York, NY 10017
(free brochure)

⚜ READING

NUTRITION

**What Every Pregnant Woman Should Know:
The Truth About Diet and Drugs in Pregnancy**
by Gail Sforza Brewer and Thomas Brewer M.D.
Random House

As You Eat So Your Baby Grows
by Nikki Goldbeck
Ceres Press
P.O. Box 87
Woodstock, NY 12498

**Pickles And Ice Cream: The Complete
Guide to Nutrition During Pregnancy**
by Mary Abbott Hess and Anne Elise Hunt
McGraw-Hill

Eating Right For Two
by Diane Klein and Rosalyn Baldamenti
Ballantine Books

PRENATAL CARE

You can send away for free literature on health hazards from:

The March of Dimes
Birth Defect Foundation
1275 Mamaroneck Avenue
White Plains, NY 10605

**Department of Health and Human Services/
National Institute on Alcohol Abuse and Alcoholism**
5600 Fishers Lane
Rockville, MD 20857

The Whole Birth Catalog: A Sourcebook for Choices in Childbirth
by Janet Isaacs Ashford
The Crossing Press

Department of Health and Human Services
Public Health Service/Food and Drug Administration
5600 Fishers Lane
Rockville, MD 20857

For $4.00 plus $1.00 postage you can send away for a "Reproductive Hazards Factpack" from:

For effective ways to quit smoking, write:

Office of Cancer Communications
National Cancer Institute
Bethseda, MD 20205

The Women's Occupational Health Resource Center
Columbia University
School of Public Health
21 Audobon Avenue
New York, NY 10034

FATHERING

Making Love During Pregnancy
Elizabeth Bing and Libby Colman
Bantam Books

Expectant Fathers
by Sam Bittman and Sue Rosenberg Zalk
E.P. Dutton

Becoming a Father: A Handbook for Expectant Fathers
By Sean Gresh
Bantam Books

The Father's Almanac
by S. Adams Sullivan
Doubleday/Dolphin

DEVELOPMENTAL BOOKS

The First Nine Months
by Geraldine Flanagan
Heinemann Medical Books

A Child is Born
By Axel-Sundberg Mirjam Furuhjelm,
and Claes Wirsen/Photos by Lennart Nilsson
Delacorte Press

EXERCISE

Jane Fonda's Workout Book for Pregnancy, Birth and Recovery
by Femmy DeLyser
Simon and Schuster

Baby Dance
by Elysa Markowitz and Howard Brainen
Prentice-Hall

Essential Exercises for the Childbearing Year
by Elizabeth Noble
Houghton Mifflin

The Complete Pregnancy Exercise Program
by Diana Simkin
New American Library

BOOKS FOR CHILDREN

These books explain how a baby is made, how a baby grows, and how a baby is born. They are aimed at children aged five and up.

So That's How I was Born
by Dr. Robert Brooks
Simon and Schuster

Where Did I Come From
by Peter Mayle
Lyle Stuart, Inc.

Where Do Babies Come From
by Margaret Sheffield
Alfred Knopf

These books deal with sibling rivalry and readjustment. They can be saved for after baby is born.

Superfudge (Ages 8 +)
by Judy Blume
E.P. Dutton

Couldn't We Have a Turtle Instead (Ages 3 +)
by Judith Vigna
Albert Whitman & Co.

Chuckie (Ages 3 +)
by Nicki Weiss
Greenwillow Books

BEAUTY AND FASHION

**Great Expectations:
How to Make 30 Easy, Fast,
Sexy, Cheerful Maternity Outfits**
by Leigh Adams and Lynda Madares
Houghton Mifflin

Newborn Beauty
by Wende Devlin Gates and
Gail McFarland Meckel
Viking Press

**A Year of Beauty and Exercise
for the Pregnant Woman**
by Judi McMahon and Zia Odell
Lippincott and Crowell

OVER-30 MOTHERS-TO-BE
Having a Baby After 30
by Elizabeth Bing and Libby Colman
Bantam Books

It's Not Too Late For A Baby
by Sylvia P. Rubin
Prentice-Hall

**The Woman Doctor's Guide to
Pregnancy Over 35**
by Dr. Kathryn Schrotenboer
Ballantine Books

BIRTH PREPARATION
**Six Practical Lessons For
An Easier Childbirth**
by Elizabeth Bing
Bantam Books

Husband Coached Childbirth
by Robert A. Bradley, M.D.
Harper & Row

Nine Months, Nine Lessons
by Gail Sforza Brewer
Simon and Schuster

Childbirth Without Fear
by Grantly Dick-Read, M.D.
Harper & Row

A Good Birth, A Safe Birth
by Diana Dorte and Roberta Scaer
Bantam Books

Choices in Childbirth
by Silvia Feldman
Bantam Books

Thank You Dr. Lamaze
by Marjorie Karmel
Harper & Row

The Experience of Childbirth
by Sheila Kitzinger
Penguin Books

Painless Childbirth
by Fernand Lamaze
Pocket Books

Birth Without Violence
by Dr. Frederick Leboyer
Alfred A. Knopf

Childbirth with Insight
by Elizabeth Noble
Houghton Mifflin

CESAREAN BIRTH

The Cesarean Birth Experience
by Bonnie Donovan
Beacon Press

**Cesarean Childbirth: A Couple's Guide
for Decision and Preparation**
by Kathleen Mitchell and Marty Nason
Harbor Publishing Co.

Cesarean Childbirth
by Christine Wilson and Wendy Hovey
New American Library

Unnecessary Cesareans: Ways to Avoid Them
by Diony Young and Charles Mahan
ICEA Bookstore
80–60 26th Avenue South
Bloomington, MN 55420

BABY NAMES

Big Book of Baby Names
by Sandra Buzbee Bailey
HP Books

The Professor's Book of First Names
by Thomas V. Busse, Ph.D.
Greenball Press
P.O. Box 29771
Elkins Park, PA 19117

**The Best Baby Name Book
in the Whole Wide World**
edited by Bruce Lansky
Meadowbrook Books

NURSERY DECORATING IDEAS

Babyspace
by Ellen Linman
Perigree Books

BREASTFEEDING BASICS

The Experience of Breastfeeding
by Sheila Kitzinger
Penguin Books

The Womanly Art of Breastfeeding
La Leche League International
9616 Minneapolis Avenue
P.O. Box 1209
Franklin Park, IL 60131–8209

Nursing Your Baby
by Karen Pryor
Pocket Books

The Tender Gift: Breastfeeding
by Dana Raphael
Schocken Books

Breastfeeding Basics
by Cecilia Worth
McGraw Hill

NOTE: La Leche League is an international network of women who promote breastfeeding and generate a variety of breastfeeding and parenting publications, including a bimonthly journal entitled *New Beginnings*.

You can call La Leche League at (312) 455-7730 or write them at the above address to obtain publications or receive the name of your nearest LLL representative, who can answer any of your breastfeeding questions.

BABY CARE

The First Twelve Months of Life
by Frank Caplan
Grosset and Dunlap

To Love a Baby
by Sandy Jones
Houghton Mifflin

Practical Parenting Tips
by Vicki Lansky
Practical Parenting
18326B Minnetonka Blvd.
Deephaven, MN 55391

Your Baby and Child
by Penelope Leach
Alfred Knopf

Baby and Child Care
by Benjamen Spock
Pocket Books

PREEMIES

Born Early
by Mary Ellen Avery
Little Brown

Beginnings
by Ellen Galinsky
Houghton Mifflin

The Premature Baby Book
by Helen Harrison
St. Martins Press

Your Premature Baby
by Robin Marantz Henig and
Anne Fletcher, M.D.
Rawson Associates

AND BABY MAKES THREE

Some interesting books on how baby can bring you closer together:

Couples with Children
by Virginia De Luca and Randy Wolfson
Warner Books

How to Stay Two When Baby Makes Three
by Marsha Dorman and Diane Klein
Prometheus Books

The Private Life of Parents
by Roberta Plutzik and Laghi Plutzik
Dodd Mead

Between Generations: The Stages of Parenthood
by Ellen Galinsky
Berkley

Your Family is Good for You
by Harvey White
Random House

CHILD CARE/WORKING BOOKLIST

For babysitters you might acquire:

Dear Babysitter
(handbook and note pad in hardcover)
by Vicki Lansky
c/o Practical Parenting
Dept. AN
18326 Mtka Boulevard
Deephaven, MN 55391

The Super Sitter
(booklet)
The U.S. Consumer Product Safety Commission
Consumer Hotline (800) 638-CPSC or (800) 638-2772

Books on child care:

The New Extended Family: Day Care Programs
by Ellen Galinsky and William Hooks
Houghton Mifflin

Who Cares for the Baby?
by Beatrice Glickman and
Nesta Bass Springer
Schocken Books

The Working Parents Guide to Child Care
by Bryna Siegel-Gorelick, Ph.D.
Little Brown

Books on being a working mother:

Help: A Handbook for Working Mothers
by Barbara Greenleaf and Dr. Lewis Schaffer
Thomas Crowell

2001 Hints for Working Mothers
Gloria Mayer
Quill

The Working Mother's Complete Handbook
by Gloria Norris and Jo Ann Miller
Dutton

The Working Parents Survival Guide
by Sally Olds
Bantam Books

BABY PLAY

Baby Learning Through Baby Play
by Ira Gordon
St. Martins Press

Loving Hands
by Dr. Frederick Leboyer
Random House

The Baby Exercise Book
by Janine Levy
Pantheon

INDEX